JOYFUL SOUNDS
The New Children's Hymnal

JOYFUL SOUNDS
The New Children's Hymnal

*Let the Word of Christ dwell in you richly
as you teach and admonish one another
in all wisdom and as you sing psalms and hymns and
spiritual songs with thankfulness in your hearts to God.*
Colossians 3:16

Publishing House
St. Louis

Library of Congress Cataloging in Publication Data

Joyful Sounds.

Includes index.
1. Sunday-schools—Hymns.
M2193.J7   783.9'52   77-13061
ISBN 0-570-01016-0

Concordia Publishing House, St. Louis, Missouri
Copyright © 1977 Concordia Publishing House

Manufactured in the United States of America

CONTENTS

*Consult Topical Index

FOREWORD

Joyful Sounds is a book of hymns and songs to help people pray, praise, and give thanks. Although the contents have been selected especially with children from ages nine to 14 in mind, it is believed that the words and tunes will appeal to persons of all ages. This collection can therefore well be used in almost any setting in which Christian people want to join in singing to their God. We hope this book will be found not only in church-school classrooms but also in homes, camps, and churches.

Music of great variety is included. There are chorales that date back to the Reformation, but also Christian folk songs that have become popular within the last decade. This rich variety of music recognizes the many moods and styles of people who just like to sing—be it a Gospel song, a black spiritual, a Christmas carol, or an evening lullaby.

Since the hymnal will be used in many differing worship settings, the number of liturgies and orders of worship is limited. Instead the hymnal includes a variety of ideas for creating worship settings to fit local needs. Yet those who prefer to follow prepared forms will find several orders of worship. The use of extemporaneous or locally prepared prayers is encouraged. However, the book does include some general and seasonal prayers and Dr. Martin Luther's morning and evening prayers. The Lord's Prayer and the Apostles' Creed appear in both the International Consultation on English Texts and the traditional versions.

The table of contents shows the arrangement of the hymns. A topical index, an alphabetical index of tunes, and an index of first lines are included at the back of the hymnal. These indexes will assist the leader and the accompanist in finding the desired selections and tunes.

This new hymnal is the result of more than 3 years of research, planning, collecting, and editing. Educators and musicians of The Lutheran Church—Missouri Synod contributed to this new resource. Members of the editorial group were E. Theo. Delaney, Earl Gaulke, Donald Hoeferkamp, Henry Niermeier, Arlon Rueter, chairman, and Rodney Schrank, secretary. Linda Preece provided valuable assistance in the preparation of the manuscript. Susan Dahl served as a consultant for The American Lutheran Church.

Joyful Sounds is presented to the church with the prayer that it will bring much pleasure to its users and great glory to our God.

Note: Those hymns for which guitar chording has been provided should be accompanied either by guitar alone or by keyboard alone.

Worship
Resources

"OH, COME, LET US WORSHIP"

WHAT IS WORSHIP?

"Let the Word of Christ dwell in you richly as you teach and admonish one another in all wisdom and as you sing psalms and hymns and spiritual songs with thankfulness in your hearts to God." (Col. 3:16)

What a dynamic description of worship! Worship begins *with God,* who speaks to us in the Word about Christ: "You are forgiven. You are My people." In our worship together, God speaks that Word to us in the Scripture readings. His Word dwells in us through faith. And like a fountain *it flows out of us to one another*—in responsive readings, in hymns, in spiritual songs. We remind one another of God's great deeds, strengthening and building up one another in our faith and life. And finally, *our worship moves upward*—in adoration of God; in thanks to Him for His mercy.

Worship becomes real as we see its three dimensions. The Word *from* God is shared *with* one another, then returns *to* God in responses of praise and thanksgiving.

SUGGESTIONS FOR WORSHIP
VARIETY IN WORSHIP

Scripture readings, songs, prayers—elements of worship—can be joined in an infinite number of ways. Worship need not be restricted to the "orders of worship" beginning on page 14.

The leader might, for example, begin by asking the assembly to pray silently for God's presence and His Spirit. Or begin with the invocation: "In the name of the Father and of the Son and of the Holy Spirit." Or begin with Luther's morning prayer (page 32), a prayer spoken extemporaneously, or a prayer written out beforehand. A student or teacher may be asked to pray (be sure to ask them beforehand).

Hymns may be included at various points in the worship—either selected beforehand by the worship leader or chosen by the students. At times a worship service might consist entirely of student-selected songs. When selecting hymns, the leader will want to consider the lesson theme or church-year season. Consult the teachers guide of your lesson materials for suggestions.

An individual class may occasionally plan and lead the worship. Or various classes could take turns offering an original prayer for coming sessions or selecting and reading a Scripture selection. Classes may also prepare visualizations of songs, create banners, or prepare other meaningful additions to the worship setting. All of these—and more—are ways the students themselves can "teach and admonish *one another* in all wisdom."

THE BIBLE
IN WORSHIP_____

Select a reading that fits with the lesson theme of the day. (Consult the teachers guide of your lesson materials for suggestions.)

Introduce the reading with a short, prefatory remark. For example, "In our lesson today we'll be thinking about a wonderful promise of God. It's written in John 15:7. . . . " Or: "Once Peter was bothered about something that probably bothers all of us. So he brought his problem to Jesus. In Matthew 18:21 we read his question and Jesus' answer."

Read the selection as a Person-to-person message—from God to us. If necessary, briefly paraphrase or explain any difficult words or phrases—as you are reading.

At times consider asking students to follow the reading in their own Bible. A moment of silent reflection after the reading helps the "Word of Christ dwell richly" in the hearer's heart.

Unison and responsive readings of psalms become more meaningful when the leader signals the purpose: "Let's remind one another of the wonder of God's creation. Psalm 8 says it so well. . . . " Or: "Maybe Jesus prayed this psalm (42) in Gethsemane. When we're scared, it's a great reminder of God's power and care. . . . "

If the students have memorized a Scripture text that fits with the lesson theme, they might repeat it in unison or responsively.

HYMNS _____

To enhance meaningful worship, select hymns that fit with the lesson theme of the day or the church year. (Consult your teachers guide for suggestions.) Include well-known hymns—hymns which, because they are already learned, allow the worshipers to concentrate their thoughts on their meaning. Ordinarily introduce no more than one "new" hymn in any worship period. Otherwise the focus of the worship period becomes overbalanced towards instruction rather than worship. A good principle to follow in teaching a new hymn: Teach both words and melody together from the start. The worship leader might begin by singing one stanza slowly; then have various groups join in singing the same stanza; boys alone, girls alone, different classes alone, all in unison.

The leader can do much to encourage hymn singing as a real expression of prayer and thanksgiving to God—and as a means of speaking the Word to one another. Here again short, prefatory remarks may help: "Let's sing a hymn that reminds us of the many ways the Holy Spirit helps us. ..." "This hymn is a quiet, thoughtful hymn, leading us to think about Jesus' suffering for our sins. ... " "This hymn rings out with all the reasons we have to worship God. ... "

PRAYER_____

Besides the prayers printed in this hymnal (page 26), many hymn stanzas may be used as spoken prayers. Use the hymn categories (Pentecost, Easter, Christmas, Witnessing, etc.) as an aid in finding hymn stanzas suitable for a given lesson-related concern or church-year theme. As in the use of hymns and Scripture readings, a few introductory words by the leader may serve as a motivation or cue for the worshiper when a printed prayer is used.

Since prayer is conversation with God, many of the prayers in a church-school worship period can be simply the expressions of the students or leader—in their own words—of thanks, adoration, confession, or petition to God, our heavenly Father. Particularly if the group is small, "circle" prayers may be used. The leader may begin with a short prayer. It could be as simple as: "Lord, be with us in our worship and study today." Other members of the assembly may pray in turn. To forestall any possible embarrassment to the shy or tongue-tied, suggest that *anyone* may simply pray: "Thank You, God." In time such spontaneous talking to God will become more natural—and will in fact contribute to a growing sense of communion with God.

As mentioned above, students may also be asked to prepare their own written prayers beforehand. Or they may be invited to suggest special requests or thanks or petitions, which the leader may include in the general prayer: "Lord, we're glad that You gave Johnny a new baby brother. Keep all of Johnny's family happy in Your love and care. ... Heavenly Father, we pray for Kevin's father, who is sick. Strengthen him in faith, and in Your own time make him well again. ... "

WHY WORSHIP?

"Oh, come, let us worship and bow down, let us kneel before our Lord, our Maker! For He is our God, and we are the people of His pasture and the sheep of His hand. He is our Redeemer and Sanctifier!"

May the hymns, the prayers, and the worship helps in this hymnal serve all who use it to worship "in spirit and in truth" Him who indeed is worthy of all praise.

"Worthy art Thou, our Lord and God, to receive glory and honor and power, for Thou didst create all things. ... Worthy is the Lamb who was slain to receive power and wealth and wisdom and might and honor and glory and blessing! ... Great and wonderful are Thy deeds, O Lord God the Almighty! Just and true are Thy ways, O King of the ages!" (Revelation 4:11; 5:12; 15:3)

ORDERS OF WORSHIP

I. General/Pentecost or Trinity Cycle

THE INVOCATION

The leader shall say:

In the name of the Father and of the Son and of the Holy Spirit. Amen.

THE OPENING HYMN

The opening hymn shall be one of praise, or it may be a morning hymn or a hymn suitable to the season or church-school lesson. All may stand.

THE SENTENCES

V. The Lord is near to all who call upon Him:

R. To all who call upon Him in truth.

V. O Lord, open Thou my lips:

R. And my mouth shall show forth Thy praise.

THE GLORIA PATRI

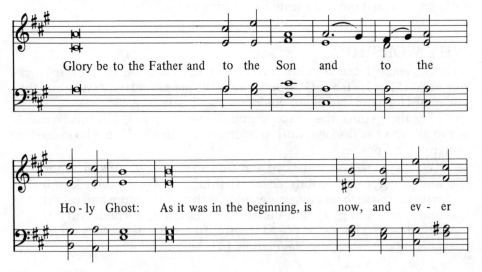

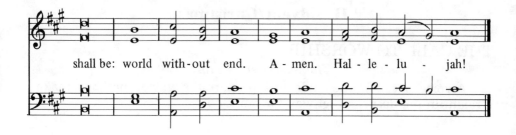

shall be: world with-out end. A - men. Hal - le - lu - jah!

THE PRAYER

A selection from the prayers, pages 26 to 33, may be read by the leader or by the group.

THE SCRIPTURE READING

A psalm or other selection of Scripture, related to the church-school lesson theme, may be read responsively or in unison. Suggested psalms: 1, 19, 23, 51, 84, 91, portion of 119, 145, 150.

THE OFFERING

THE HYMN

Choose a hymn related to the church-school lesson theme.

THE CLASS PERIOD

THE CLOSING HYMN

All shall stand

THE BENEDICTION

The grace of our Lord Jesus Christ, the love of God, and the communion of the Holy Spirit be with you all. Amen.

SILENT PRAYER

II. Advent/Christmas

THE CALL TO WORSHIP

The leader shall say:

A voice cries: "In the wilderness prepare the way of the Lord, make straight in the desert a highway for our God."

THE OPENING HYMN

The opening hymn shall be one suitable to the season.

THE SENTENCES

V. Every valley shall be lifted up, and every mountain and hill be made low:

R. The uneven ground shall become level, and the rough places a plain.

V. And the glory of the Lord shall be revealed, and all flesh shall see it together:

R. For the mouth of the Lord has spoken.

V. Get you up to a high mountain, O Zion, herald of good tidings:

R. O Jerusalem, herald of good tidings, lift it up; fear not.

V. Lift it up, fear not:

R. He will gather the lambs in His arms, He will carry them in His bosom.

THE GLORIA PATRI

Glo - ry be to the Fa-ther and to the Son and to the Ho - ly Ghost;

As it was in the be-ginning, is now, and ev-er shall be, world without end. A-men.

THE PRAYER

An Advent or Christmas prayer, page 26, may be read by the leader or by the group.

THE SCRIPTURE READING

A psalm or other selection of Scripture, related to the church-school lesson of the day, may be read responsively or in unison. Suggested psalms: 8, 67, 96, 100, 121.

THE HYMN

Choose a hymn related to the church-school lesson theme.

THE CLASS PERIOD

THE CLOSING HYMN

All shall stand

THE CLOSING PRAYER

To be said in unison

God be merciful to us and bless us and cause His face to shine upon us. Amen.

III. Epiphany

THE CALL TO WORSHIP

The leader shall say:

Make a joyful noise unto God, all ye lands: sing forth the honor of His name; make His praise glorious.

THE MORNING PRAYER

Luther's Morning Prayer (page 32)

THE OPENING HYMN

The opening hymn shall be one suitable to the season.

THE SCRIPTURE READING

A psalm or other selection of Scripture, related to the church-school lesson, may be read by the leader or by the group.

THE OFFERING

THE HYMN

Choose a hymn related to the church-school lesson theme.

THE PRAYER

THE CLASS PERIOD

THE NUNC DIMITTIS

Lord, now lettest Thou Thy servant de - part in peace ac -

cord-ing to Thy word, For mine eyes have seen Thy Salvation:

which Thou hast pre - pared be - fore the face of all people,
a Light to light - en the Gen - tiles and the Glo - ry of Thy
peo - ple Is - - - ra - el. Glo - ry be to the Father and
to the Son and to the Ho - ly Ghost; As it was in the be -
ginning, is now, and ev - er shall be, world with - out end. A - men.

THE BLESSING

May the God of hope fill you with all joy and peace in believing, so that by the power of the Holy Spirit you may abound in hope. Amen.

IV. Lent

THE CALL TO WORSHIP

The leader shall say:

Christ became obedient unto death, even the death of the cross. Oh, come, let us worship Him!

THE HYMN

The opening hymn shall be one suitable to the season.

THE SENTENCES

V. If we say that we have no sin, we deceive ourselves, and the truth is not in us:

R. If we confess our sins, He is faithful and just to forgive us our sins and to cleanse us from all unrighteousness.

THE PRAYER

A Lenten prayer, page 27, may be said by the leader or by the group.

THE OFFERING

THE HYMN

Choose a hymn related to the church-school lesson theme.

THE CLASS PERIOD

THE AGNUS DEI

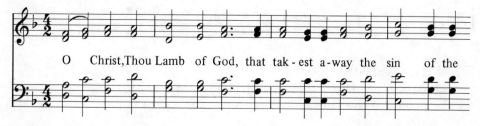

O Christ, Thou Lamb of God, that tak-est a-way the sin of the

world, have mer- cy up-on us. O Christ, Thou Lamb of God, that

tak - est a-way the sin of the world, have mer- cy up - on us.

O Christ, Thou Lamb of God, that tak- est a-way the sin of the

world, grant us Thy peace. A - - - - men.

THE BENEDICTION

The grace of our Lord Jesus Christ be with you all. Amen.

V. Easter

THE INVOCATION
In the name of our risen Lord and Savior. Amen.

THE OPENING HYMN

THE SENTENCES
V. This is the day which the Lord has made:

R. We will rejoice and be glad in it.

V. He is risen!

R. The Lord is risen indeed. Alleluia!

V. Oh, sing unto the Lord a new song:

R. For He has done marvelous things.

V. Our Lord Jesus said: I am the Resurrection and the Life; he who believes in Me, though he die, yet shall he live:

R. And whoever lives and believes in Me shall never die.

THE EASTER HYMN OF PRAISE

THE PRAYER
An Easter prayer is on page 27 or 28

THE CREED
The Apostles' Creed may be spoken (page 25)

THE OFFERING

THE CLASS PERIOD

THE CLOSING HYMN

THE DOXOLOGY

VI. Pentecost

THE INVOCATION

The leader may say:

Holy Spirit, hear us
On this sacred day;
Come to us with blessing,
Come with us to stay.

THE OPENING HYMN

THE SENTENCES

V. As many as are led by the Spirit of God:

R. They are the sons of God.

V. Our Lord Jesus said: The Comforter, who is the Holy Spirit, whom the Father will send in My name:

R. He shall teach you all things and bring all things to your remembrance.

V. He shall testify of Me:

R. He will guide you into all truth. He shall glorify Me.

V. Come, Holy Spirit, and fill the hearts of Your faithful people:

R. And kindle in them the fire of Your love.

THE SCRIPTURE READING

RESPONSIVE PRAYER

The following or some other suitable prayer may be used:

Leader: Let us pray for the gift of the Holy Spirit, that He may open our eyes to the truth that Jesus is our living Lord and Savior and that we may always walk in the light of that truth.

Response: Lord God, grant us Your Holy Spirit, through Jesus Christ. Your Son, our Lord.

Leader: Let us ask God to send His Holy Spirit into the hearts of all men, that the whole world may be brought out of the darkness of sin into the light which only Christ can give, that they too may receive forgiveness of sins and life everlasting.

Response: O God, send forth Your Spirit, and turn away many from darkness to light.

Leader: Let us pray to God for the blessings of His Spirit: the Spirit of widsom and knowledge, of grace and prayer, of power and strength, of sanctification and the fear of God.

Response: Grant us the blessings of Your Spirit, O God.

Leader: Let us also ask God to produce in us the fruits of the Spirit. The fruits of the Spirit are love, joy, peace, patience, kindness, goodness, faithfulness, gentleness, self-control.

Response: If we live in the Spirit, let us also walk in the Spirit.

THE PRAYER

A prayer for the Holy Spirit is on page 28

THE OFFERING

THE HYMN

THE CLASS PERIOD

THE CLOSING HYMN

All shall stand

THE BENEDICTION

The grace of the Lord Jesus Christ and the love of God and the communion of the Holy Spirit be with you all. Amen.

THE APOSTLES' CREED

I believe in God the Father Almighty, Maker of heaven and earth. And in Jesus Christ, His only Son, our Lord, who was conceived by the Holy Ghost, born of the Virgin Mary, suffered under Pontius Pilate, was crucified, dead, and buried; He descended into hell; the third day He rose again from the dead; He ascended into heaven, and sitteth on the right hand of God the Father Almighty; from thence He shall come to judge the quick and the dead. I believe in the Holy Ghost; the holy Christian Church, the communion of saints; the forgiveness of sins; the resurrection of the body; and the life everlasting. Amen.

OR

I believe in God, the Father almighty,
　　creator of heaven and earth.
I believe in Jesus Christ, His only Son, our Lord.
　　He was conceived by the power of the Holy Spirit
　　　and born of the Virgin Mary.
　　He suffered under Pontius Pilate,
　　　was crucified, died, and was buried.
　　He descended into hell.
　　On the third day He rose again.
　　He ascended into heaven
　　　and is seated at the right hand of the Father.
　　He will come to judge the living and the dead.
I believe in the Holy Spirit,
　　the holy catholic church,
　　the communion of saints,
　　the forgiveness of sins,
　　the resurrection of the body,
　　and the life everlasting. Amen.

PRAYERS

ADVENT

Dear heavenly Father, we remember Your gracious promises to people long ago. You promised to send a Savior, and You kept that promise by sending Your dear Son, Jesus Christ. Thank You that He became a human being to save us from sin and hell. Help us to be thankful for the sacrifice He made. Make us able to live each day waiting for Jesus to come again and take us to Himself in heaven. Hear us for Jesus' sake. Amen.

CHRISTMAS

1 _____

Dear Father in heaven, thank You for Christmas. We're glad we can celebrate Jesus' birthday every year. We'd like to give Him beautiful presents, but we can't. So we give Him our love. And we give presents to our friends as a sign of our love for Him.

Happy birthday, Jesus! We love You. Thank You for coming to earth to be our Savior. Thank You for bringing joy to the whole world. Please help us share this joy. Amen.

2 _____

Blessed Christ Child, we wish we could have knelt at Your manger bed so many years ago. We know that even as a weak and helpless baby You were the almighty Son of God by whom the world was made. You loved us very much. And You showed that love by becoming a child in order to save us from sin and hell. Thank You for Your grace and mercy. Dear Jesus, live in our hearts. Cleanse us from sin, and help us serve You every day of our life. Fill us with love toward one another, and make us willing to share all the blessings You have given us. Amen.

EPIPHANY

1 _____

Praise and honor to You, heavenly Father, for offering the promises of Your love to all people in the world.

Praise and honor to You, dear Jesus, for being the Light of the whole world.

Praise and honor to You, Holy Spirit, for blessing the work of pastors, teachers, and missionaries and for bringing people everywhere into the Christian family.

We are glad we know You. We're glad we belong to Your family. Give us joy in worshiping You, Lord. May we, like the Wise Men, bring You gifts of love. We want everyone everywhere to know You. May we, like the star, point others to You. Amen.

2 _____

Thank You, heavenly Father, for guiding the Wise Men by a wonderful star to the house where Jesus, our Savior-King, lay. When we hear about Your mercy to these Wise Men from a distant land, we remember that Jesus came to save everyone everywhere. We confess Jesus as our Savior, and we worship Him as our God and King. We pray too that the good news of forgiveness and salvation may be spread throughout the world so that all people may know Your love for them. In Jesus' name. Amen.

LENT

1 _____

Dear Jesus, when I think of Your suffering and death, I'm filled with both joy and sadness. Joy because I know You suffered and died so my sins could be forgiven. Sadness because I so often sin against You. Joy because I know that You have earned for me a place in heaven. Sadness because I don't always show by my life that heaven is my home. Thank You, Jesus, that You are so ready to forgive the wrongs I do. Let me remember that Your sacrifice on the cross was for all people—that Your love is for everyone. Help me to love others as You have loved me. Amen.

2 _____

Lord Jesus, thank You for Your great love that led You to suffer and die to save us and all people from the curse and punishment of sin. Lead us to know our sin and to be sorry for the ways we have disobeyed You. Strengthen our faith and love for You as we remember how You were beaten, crowned with thorns, and crucified. Help us show our love by avoiding sin and doing those things that are well-pleasing to You. Lord Jesus, thank You for giving Yourself to us. Help us give ourselves to You and live as Your children. Amen.

EASTER

1 _____

Dear Jesus, thank You for rising from the grave on Easter morning. Now we are sure that our sins are forgiven. Thank You! When we are lonely or afraid, remind us that You are with us. Thank You for Your promise to give us life with You forever. Amen.

Lord Jesus Christ, our risen Savior, we're so happy on this glorious Easter Day because You rose from the dead. Now we are sure that our sins are forgiven and that we will live forever with You. We thank and praise You, blessed Savior, for earning our salvation by suffering and dying on the cross. Help us remember that You are the ever-living Savior to whom we may come in every trouble and temptation. Keep us in Your love. When it is Your will, take us to heaven, where we shall live with You forever. Amen.

PENTECOST

Dear Jesus, when You went back to heaven, You promised to send the Holy Spirit to live in Your people on earth. Thank You for keeping that promise at the first Pentecost. And thank You for giving us the Holy Spirit.

O Holy Spirit, we thank You for giving us faith in Jesus. Thank You for giving us love and joy and peace. Please help us grow in love for Jesus and for one another. Bless us as we study Your Word, and help us understand what it means for our lives today. Thank You for hearing our prayer. Amen.

BIRTHDAY

Dear Lord, thank You for my life—and for another birthday. Help me grow bigger and stronger. Help me grow in understanding and wisdom. Help me to grow in faith and to trust Your loving care for me. Thank You for my family and friends, through whom Your love comes to me. Bless them with every good thing. In Jesus' name I pray. Amen.

EVANGELISM/MISSION

Dear Jesus, we remember Your command to make all people Your disciples. Thank You for trusting us to tell people about Your love for them. Please lead us to those in our neighborhood who need to hear about You. Help us to be friends with them, and give us the right words to say so they may love you too.

Bless the missionaries all around the world. Please take care of them and their families, and give them joy in their work. Be with all of us as we share Your love. Amen.

CHURCH

Dear God, we're so glad to be here today! We love You. And we like to praise and worship You. Bless our teachers and our pastor. And bless everyone who helps take care of this building. Help us listen carefully to Your Word. Hear the prayers we offer, and send the Holy Spirit to guide our praises. Help us to love one another as You love us. We pray in Jesus' name. Amen.

HOME/FAMILY

Dear Lord, thank You for giving us people to love and to be loved by. Thank You for the people who live at our house. Give us Your kind of love for one another. Help us to be forgiving, kind, and true. Especially we ask that You would keep us close to You. Give us joy in reading Your Word and praising You together. Protect us in times of danger, and keep us trusting You at all times.

Come, Lord Jesus, be our Guest! Amen.

PATRIOTIC

Lord of all people and nations, thank You for our country. Please bless all the people in our land. Give us the kind of weather we need for food to grow. Protect us in time of storms, and keep us safe in time of war. Guide our leaders to rule wisely and well. Make the people willing to be good citizens and helpful neighbors, so Your name may be glorified. Give us peace, so that Your Word may be taught freely throughout our land. We ask all these blessings in Jesus' name. Amen.

FOR SOMEONE WHO IS ILL

Lord Jesus, You know that _____ is sick (hurt). You know how to heal (him/her) and we ask You to do it. Take away (his/her) pain and tiredness. Make (his/her) body strong again. Please bless everyone who helps take care of (him/her). Remind (him/her) of Your great love. Help (him/her) remember that You are always with (him/her). Show us how to help (him/her) with Your love.

Thank You, Jesus, for hearing our prayer. Amen.

GENERAL

1 _____

Dear heavenly Father, thank You for inviting us to study Your Word, to tell You our needs, and to learn more about living as Christians. Help us remember that You are here with us. Help us to pay attention as we listen and learn. Help us to understand Your Word, remember it, and live according to Your will. Hear us for Jesus' sake. Amen.

2 _____

Dear heavenly Father, thank You for giving us parents to care for us. Thank You for clothing, food, and a place to live. Thank You for the Bible, from which we learn about Your love for us. May we love Your Holy Word. By the power of Your Spirit help us believe in Jesus and follow His example. Hear us for Jesus' sake. Amen.

3 _____

Thank You, Lord, for the blessings You have given us through the church. We praise You for Your holy Word, which tells us about the Savior who died for us. Bless our parents and teachers who explain Your Word. Teach us how to obey You. Help us also to serve one another. In Jesus' name we pray. Amen.

4 _____

Lord Jesus, You are the Good Shepherd. You laid down Your life to save us from our sins. We thank You for Your great love. Feed us in the green pastures of Your love as we study Your Word. Help us to grow in knowledge, faith, and holiness. When we stray into sin, bring us back to Your fold. Keep us faithful to You and let us live with You forever. Amen.

5 _____

Dear Jesus, You have said, "Let the children come to Me." We are happy to know that You love us and want us to be Your children. Thank You for our parents and all others who have taught us to know You. Keep us, dear Lord, from harm and danger. When we are tempted to do wrong, make us strong to do what is right. Help us to love and understand Your Word and to obey it. Have mercy on the children who still don't know You. Help us tell those children how much You want them to come to You. Amen.

6 _____

Dear Lord, You are our God and Savior. You are our mighty King. And You are our Friend. We are thankful that You forgive us when we do wrong and when we fail to do right. Keep us humble, trusting in Your grace and mercy. But make us bold too! Bold to live for You by serving others. Bold to speak Your Word. Bold to be known as Christians wherever we go. We want to learn more about You and how to serve You. Bless our class time today. Speak to us through our pastors and teachers.

Give us attentive minds and willing hearts. Be present in our classes. Teach us the truths You want us to know. We pray in Jesus' name. Amen.

7_____

Dear Lord, You have invited us to pray about everything. Thank You. We believe Your promise to hear the prayers we offer in Jesus' name.

We pray, Lord, that You would give us mercy and forgive our sins by which we have offended You:

Lord, hear our prayer.

Bring an end to quarreling and fighting among people on earth, and give us grace to live in peace with one another:

Lord, hear our prayer.

Help us work and play in such a way that all our activities may bring honor to Your name:

Lord, hear our prayer.

Watch over the sick, the troubled, the lonely people of the world, and let them experience the strength and joy Your Spirit gives:

Lord, hear our prayer.

Give peace to our nation; protect us from war and violence, and give us hope in times of disaster:

Lord, hear our prayer.

Bless our church and school, our pastor and teachers, and all others who serve in this place:

Lord, hear our prayer.

Guard our homes and families with Your love, and make us loving and considerate of one another:

Lord, hear our prayer.

All these blessings we are bold to ask because You have given us the greatest blessing of all—Yourself. And we would give You ourselves. We love because You first loved us. Amen.

8_____

In the name of our God—Father, Son, and Holy Spirit. Amen.

For making the world and all that is in it good:

Thank You, God.

For making us and giving us wonderful bodies and minds:

Thank You, God.

For wanting us to be happy and to enjoy the world You made:

Thank You, God.

For the homes we have and the people who love and care for us:

Thank You, God.

For food to eat and people who prepare it:
Thank You, God.

For friends with whom we work and play:
Thank You, God.

For leading us to know You are our Friend and Savior:
Thank You, God.

For Baptism and for the gift of the Holy Spirit:
Thank You, God.

For church and Sunday school where, together with our friends, we can worship and praise You:
Thank You, God.

For everything we thank You, God.
In Jesus' name. Amen.

LUTHER'S MORNING PRAYER

I thank Thee, my heavenly Father, through Jesus Christ, Thy dear Son, that Thou hast kept me this night from all harm and danger; and I pray Thee that Thou wouldst keep me this day also from sin and every evil, that all my doings and life may please Thee. For into Thy hands I commend myself, my body and soul, and all things. Let Thy holy angel be with me that the wicked foe may have no power over me. Amen.

OR

We give thanks to You, heavenly Father, through Jesus Christ, Your dear Son, that You have protected us through the night from all danger and harm. We ask You to preserve and keep us this day also from all sin and evil, that in all our thoughts, words, and deeds we may serve and please You. Into Your hands we commend our bodies and souls and all that is ours. Let Your holy angels have charge of us that the wicked one have no power over us. Amen.

LUTHER'S EVENING PRAYER

I thank Thee, my heavenly Father, through Jesus Christ, Thy dear Son, that Thou hast graciously kept me this day; and I pray Thee that Thou wouldst forgive me all my sins, where I have done wrong, and graciously keep me this night. For into Thy hands I commend myself, my body and soul, and all things. Let Thy holy angel be with me that the wicked foe may have no power over me. Amen.

OR

We give thanks to You, heavenly Father, through Jesus Christ, Your dear Son, that You have this day so graciously protected us. We beg You to forgive us all our sins and the wrong which we have done. By Your great mercy defend us from all the perils and dangers of this night. Into Your hands we commend our bodies and souls and all that is ours. Let Your holy angels have charge of us that the wicked one have no power over us. Amen.

THE LORD'S PRAYER

Our Father who art in heaven, Hallowed be Thy name. Thy kingdom come. They will be done on earth as it is in heaven. Give us this day our daily bread. And forgive us our trespasses as we forgive those who trespass against us. And lead us not into temptation, but deliver us from evil. For Thine is the kingdom and the power and the glory forever and ever. Amen.

OR

Our Father in heaven,
   hallowed be Your name,
   Your kingdom come,
   Your will be done
     on earth as in heaven.
Give us today our daily bread.
Forgive us our sins
   as we forgive those who sin against us.
Save us from the time of trial,
   and deliver us from evil.
For the kingdom, the power, and the glory are Yours
   now and forever. Amen.

The Christmas Cycle

1   # Lift Up Your Heads, Ye Mighty Gates

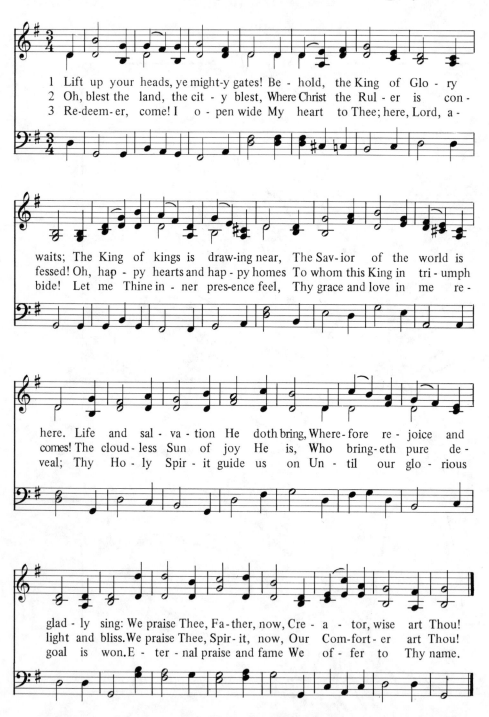

1 Lift up your heads, ye might-y gates! Be - hold, the King of Glo - ry waits; The King of kings is draw-ing near, The Sav-ior of the world is here. Life and sal - va - tion He doth bring, Where-fore re - joice and glad - ly sing: We praise Thee, Fa - ther, now, Cre - a - tor, wise art Thou!

2 Oh, blest the land, the cit - y blest, Where Christ the Rul - er is con - fessed! Oh, hap - py hearts and hap - py homes To whom this King in tri - umph comes! The cloud - less Sun of joy He is, Who bring-eth pure de - light and bliss. We praise Thee, Spir - it, now, Our Com-fort - er art Thou!

3 Re-deem - er, come! I o - pen wide My heart to Thee; here, Lord, a - bide! Let me Thine in - ner pres-ence feel, Thy grace and love in me re - veal; Thy Ho - ly Spir - it guide us on Un - til our glo - rious goal is won. E - ter - nal praise and fame We of - fer to Thy name.

Text: *Georg Weissel (1590—1635); trans. Catherine Winkworth (1829—78), alt.*
Tune: **Macht hoch die Tür,** *August Lemke (1820—1913)*

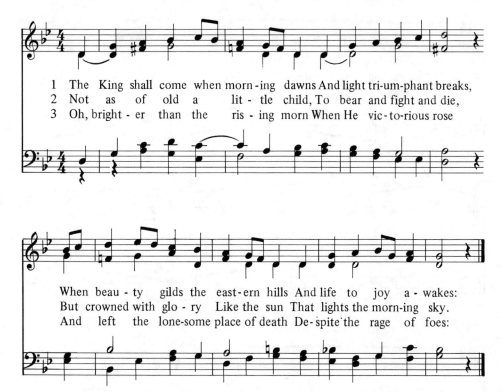

1 The King shall come when morn-ing dawns And light tri-um-phant breaks,
2 Not as of old a lit - tle child, To bear and fight and die,
3 Oh, bright - er than the ris - ing morn When He vic-to-rious rose

When beau - ty gilds the east-ern hills And life to joy a - wakes:
But crowned with glo - ry Like the sun That lights the morn-ing sky.
And left the lone-some place of death De-spite the rage of foes:

4 Oh, brighter than that glorious morn
   Shall this fair morning be,
   When Christ, our King, in beauty comes
   And we His face shall see!

5 The King shall come when morning dawns
   And light and beauty brings.
   Hail, Christ the Lord! Thy people pray:
   Come quickly, King of kings.

Text: *John Brownlie (1859—1925), cento*
Tune: **Consolation** (Kentucky Harmony, *1816)*
Setting: *Theodore Beck (1929—   )*

1 Oh, come, oh, come, Em-man - u - el, And ran-som cap-tive
2 Oh, come, Thou Rod of Jes - se, free Thine own from Sa-tan's

Is - ra - el That mourns in lone-ly ex - ile here
tyr - an-ny; From depths of hell Thy peo - ple save,

Un - til the Son of God ap -pear. Re-joice! Re-joice!
And give them vic - t'ry o'er the grave. Re-joice! Re-joice!

Em-man - u - el Shall come to thee, O Is - ra - el.
Em-man - u - el Shall come to thee, O Is - ra - el.

Text: *Anonymous Latin; trans. John Mason Neale (1818—66), cento*
Tune: **Veni, Emmanuel** *(Plainsong melody)*
Setting: *Paul Bunjes (1914—)*

1 On Jor - dan's banks the Bap - tist's cry An - noun - ces
2 Then cleansed be ev - 'ry life from sin, Make straight the
3 We hail You as our Sav - ior, Lord, Our Ref - uge

that the Lord is nigh; A - wake and hear - ken, for he
way for God with - in; And let us all our hearts pre -
and our great Re - ward; With - out Your grace we waste a -

brings Glad tid - ings of the King of kings.
pare For Christ to come and en - ter there.
way Like flow'rs that with - er and de - cay.   A - men.

4 Stretch forth Your hand, our health restore,
   And make us rise to fall no more;
   Oh, let Your face upon us shine
   And fill the world with love divine.

5 All praise to You, eternal Son,
   Whose advent has our freedom won,
   Whom with the Father we adore,
   And Holy Spirit, evermore.

Text: Charles Coffin (1676—1749), cento; trans. John Chandler (1806–76), alt.
*Tune: **Puer nobis nascitur** (Musae Sioniae, VI, 1609)*

Savior of the Nations, Come

1 Sav - ior of the na - tions, come; Vir - gin's Son, make
2 Not by hu - man flesh and blood, By the Spir - it
3 Now Thy man - ger's ha - lo bright Hal - lows night with
4 Praise to God the Fa - ther sing, Praise to God the

here Thy home! Mar - vel now, O heav'n and earth,
of our God Was the Word of God made flesh,
new - born light; Let no night this light sub - due,
Son, our King, Praise to God the Spir - it be

That the Lord chose such a birth.
Wom - an's Off-spring, pure and fresh.
Let our faith shine ev - er new.
Ev - er and e - ter - nal - ly. A - men.

Text: Ascr. St. Ambrose (340—97), cento; trans. sts.1, 2, 4, William M. Reynolds (1812—76),
    st. 3, Martin L. Seltz (1909—67)
Tune: **Nun komm, der Heiden Heiland** *(Geystliche gesangk Buchleyn,* Wittenberg, *1524), adapted*
Setting: Jan Bender (1909—   )

1 Pre-pare the way, O Zi-on! Ye aw-ful deeps, rise high, Sink
2 O Zi-on, He ap-proach-es, Your Lord and King for aye, Strew
3 Fling wide your por-tal, Zi-on, To hail your glo-rious King! His

low, ye tow'r-ing moun-tains, The Lord is draw-ing nigh, The
palms where He ad-vanc-es, Spread gar-ments in His way. God's
tid-ings of sal-va-tion To ev-'ry peo-ple bring, Who,

righ-teous King of Glo-ry Fore-told in sa-cred sto-ry,
prom-ise fail-eth nev-er, Ho-san-na and for-ev-er, Oh,
wait-ing yet in sad-ness, Would sing His praise in glad-ness.

blest is He that came In God the Fa-ther's name!

Text: Franz M. Franzen (1772—1847), cento; trans. Augustus Nelson (1863—1949), alt.
Tune: **Bereden vaeg foer Herran** *(Swedish melody)*
Setting: Healey Willan (1880—1968)

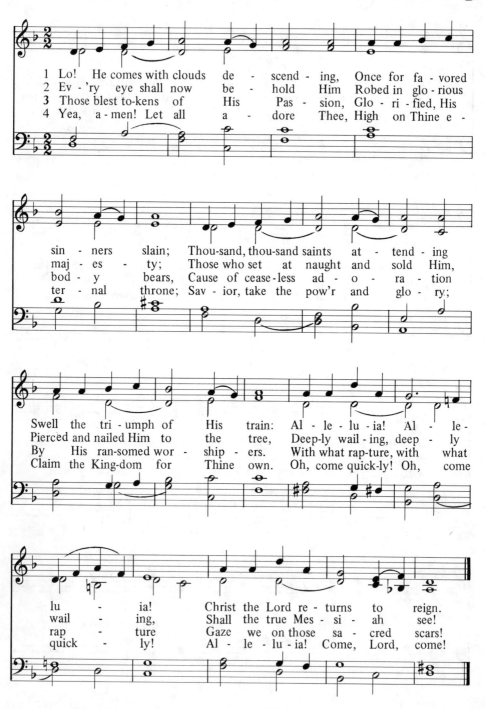

1 Lo! He comes with clouds descending, Once for favored sinners slain; Thousand, thousand saints attending Swell the triumph of His train: Alleluia! Alleluia! Christ the Lord returns to reign.

2 Ev'ry eye shall now behold Him Robed in glorious majesty; Those who set at naught and sold Him, Pierced and nailed Him to the tree, Deeply wailing, deeply wailing, Shall the true Messiah see!

3 Those blest tokens of His Passion, Glorified, His body bears, Cause of ceaseless adoration By His ransomed worshipers. With what rapture, with what rapture Gaze we on those sacred scars!

4 Yea, amen! Let all adore Thee, High on Thine eternal throne; Savior, take the pow'r and glory; Claim the Kingdom for Thine own. Oh, come quickly! Oh, come quickly! Alleluia! Come, Lord, come!

Text: *Charles Wesley (1707—88), alt.*
Tune: **Picardy** *(traditional French carol)*
Setting: *Paul Bunjes (1914—)*

Child in the Manger

1 Child in the man - ger, In - fant of Ma - ry; Out - cast and
2 Once the most ho - ly, Child of sal - va - tion, Gent - ly and
3 Proph-ets fore - told Him, In - fant of won - der; An - gels be -

Stran - ger, Lord of all, Child who in - her - its all our trans-
low - ly lived be - low; Now as our glo - rious, might - y Re -
hold Him on His throne; Wor - thy our Sav - ior of all their

gres - sions, All our de - mer - its on Him fall.
deem - er, See Him vic - to - rious o'er each foe.
prais - es; Hap - py for - ev - er are His own.

Text: Mary Macdonald (1817—90); trans. Lachlan Macbean (1853—1931)
Tune: Bunessan (traditional Gaelic melody)
Setting: Healey Willan (1880—1968)

Refrain

Go, tell it on the moun - tain, O-ver the hills and ev - 'ry- where;

Go, tell it on the moun - tain That Je - sus Christ is born.

1 While shep-herds kept their watch-ing O'er si - lent flocks by night,
2 The shep-herds feared and trem-bled, When lo, a - bove the earth
3 Down in a low - ly man-ger Our hum-ble Christ was born,

Be - hold,thru-out the heav-ens There shone a ho - ly light;
Rang out the an - gel cho - rus That hailed our Sav-ior's birth;
And God sent us sal - va - tion That bless-ed Christ-mas morn;

Text: American spiritual, cento
*Tune: **Go tell it** (American Negro spiritual)*

1 An-gels we have heard on high, Sweet-ly sing-ing o'er the plains,
2 Shep-herds, why this ju - bi-lee? Why your joy-ous strains pro-long?
3 Come to Beth - le - hem and see Him whose birth the an - gels sing;
4 Glo - ry to the Fa - ther be, Glo - ry, Vir-gin-born, to Thee,

And the moun-tains in re-ply Ech - o - ing their joy - ous strains:
What the glad-some tid - ings be Which in-spire your heav'n - ly song?
Come, a - dore on bend - ed knee Christ the Lord, the new - born King.
Glo - ry to the Ho - ly Ghost, Praised by men and heav'n - ly host:

Glo - - - - - ri - a

in ex - cel - sis De - o! Glo - - -

- - ri - a in ex - cel - sis De - o!

Text: 18th-century French carol, cento; trans. Crown of Jesus, *1862, alt.*
Tune: **Gloria** *(traditional French carol)*
Setting: Paul Bunjes (1914—)

1 Come a-long with me   to Beth-le-hem To   see the Ba - by there.
2 Come a-long with me   to Beth-le-hem, Out   on that star - ry plain
3 Come a-long with me   to Beth-le-hem, Where Wise Men from a - far

Come a-long with me   to wor-ship Him, The Christ Child pure and fair.
Where shep-herds gath-ered round to hear The an - gels' glad re - frain.
Were   shown the way to the man-ger side By a bright - ly shin - ing star.

For   Je - sus is God's Son, you know, Sent down here from a - bove
"Glo - ry   to God on high," they sang, "And peace on earth to men."
They brought the Christ Child frank-in - cense And gold and myrrh gifts too.

To   be our Lord and Sav - ior too, To teach us of God's love.
Come a-long with me to Beth-le - hem, Where hope is born a - gain.
Come a-long with me, you wise men all, And give the gift of "you."

Text: Frank W. Klos (1924—)
Tune: Frank W. Klos (1924—)
Setting: R. Harold Terry (1925—)

1 Ev-'ry year the Christ Child Comes to earth a-gain
2 He would with His bless-ing In each home a-bide
3 All un-seen, the Sav-ior At my side does stand,

To pre-pare His man-ger With the sons of men.
And on ev-'ry path-way Trav-el by our side.
Ev-er-more to guide me With His lov-ing hand.

Text: Johann Wilhelm Hey (1789—1854); trans. W. Gustave Polack (1890—1950)
Tune: Alle Jahre wieder, J.C.H. Rinck (1770—1846)

God is here — let's celebrate!
With song and with dance,
    with stringed instruments and brass,
    with cymbals and drums,
   let us express ecstatic joy in God's presence.

(Psalm 33)

1 "From heav'n a-bove to earth I come To
bear good news to ev-'ry home; Glad tid-ings of great
joy I bring, Where-of I now will say and sing:

2 "To you this night is born a child Of
Ma-ry, cho-sen vir-gin mild; This lit-tle child, of
low-ly birth, Shall be the joy of all the earth.

3 "This is the Christ, our God and Lord, Who
in all need shall aid af-ford; He will Him-self your
Sav-ior be From all your sins to set you free.

4 "He will on you the gifts be-stow Prepared by God for all be-low, That in His king-dom,
bright and fair, You may with us His glo-ry share."

5 Ah, dearest Jesus, holy Child,
Make Thee a bed, soft, undefiled,
Within my heart, that it may be
A quiet chamber kept for Thee.

6 My heart for very joy doth leap,
My lips no more can silence keep;
I, too, must sing with joyful tongue
That sweetest ancient cradlesong:

7 Glory to God in highest heaven,
Who unto us His Son hath given!
While angels sing with pious mirth
A glad new year to all the earth.

Text: Martin Luther (1483—1546),cento; trans. Catherine Winkworth (1827—78), alt.
*Tune: **Vom Himmel hoch** (Geistliche Lieder, Leipzig, 1539)*

1 Gen-tle Ma-ry laid her Child Low-ly in a man - ger;
2 An - gels sang a - bout His birth, Wise Men sought and found Him;
3 Gen - tle Ma-ry laid her Child Low-ly in a man - ger;

There He lay, the Un-de-filed, To the world a stran - ger.
Heav-en's star shone brightly forth, Glo-ry all a - round Him.
He is still the Un-de-filed, But no more a stran - ger.

Such a babe in such a place, Can He be the Sav - ior?
Shep-herds saw the won-drous sight, Heard the an-gels sing - ing;
Son of God of hum-ble birth, Beau-ti - ful the sto - ry;

Ask the saved of all the race Who have found His fa - vor.
All the plains were lit that night, All the hills were ring - ing.
Praise His name in all the earth; Hail! the King of Glo - ry!

Text: Joseph Simpson Cook (1859—1933)
*Tune: **Tempus adest floridum** (Piae Cantiones, 1582)*
Setting: Theodore Beck (1929—)

1 Good Chris-tian men, re-joice,   With heart and soul and   voice;
2 Good Chris-tian men, re-joice,   With heart and soul and   voice;
3 Good Chris-tian men, re-joice,   With heart and soul and   voice;

Give   ye heed to   what we say;   Je - sus Christ is born   to-day;
Now   ye hear of   end - less bliss: Je - sus Christ was born for this!
Now   ye need not fear the grave;   Je - sus Christ was born to save!

Ox   and ass   be - fore Him bow, And He is in   the man-ger now.
He   hath oped the heav'n-ly door, And man is blessed for - ev - er-more.
Calls you one and calls you all   To   gain His ev - er - last - ing hall.

Christ is born to - day!   Christ is born to - day!
Christ was born for this!   Christ was born for this!
Christ was born to save!   Christ was born to save!

Text: *Medieval Latin carol; trans. John Mason Neale (1818—66)*
Tune: **In dulci jubilo** *(14th-century carol; Klug's* Geistliche Lieder, *Wittenberg, 1535)*

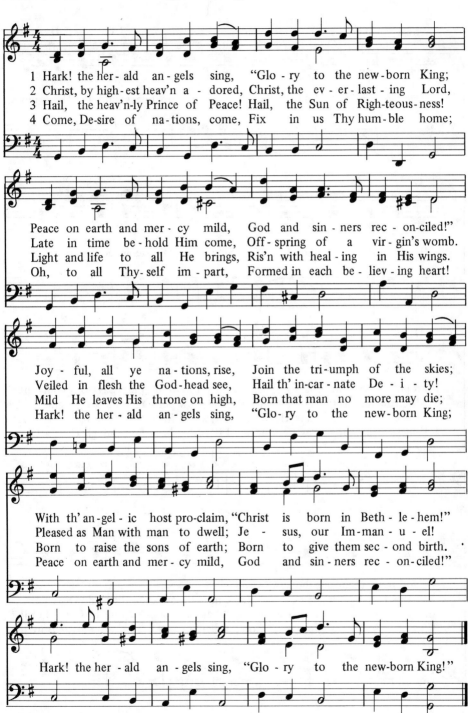

1 Hark! the her-ald an-gels sing, "Glo-ry to the new-born King;
2 Christ, by high-est heav'n a - dored, Christ, the ev - er - last - ing Lord,
3 Hail, the heav'n-ly Prince of Peace! Hail, the Sun of Righ-teous-ness!
4 Come, De-sire of na-tions, come, Fix in us Thy hum-ble home;

Peace on earth and mer - cy mild, God and sin - ners rec - on-ciled!"
Late in time be - hold Him come, Off - spring of a vir - gin's womb.
Light and life to all He brings, Ris'n with heal - ing in His wings.
Oh, to all Thy-self im - part, Formed in each be - liev - ing heart!

Joy - ful, all ye na - tions, rise, Join the tri-umph of the skies;
Veiled in flesh the God-head see, Hail th' in-car - nate De - i - ty!
Mild He leaves His throne on high, Born that man no more may die;
Hark! the her - ald an - gels sing, "Glo-ry to the new-born King;

With th' an-gel - ic host pro-claim, "Christ is born in Beth - le - hem!"
Pleased as Man with man to dwell; Je - sus, our Im-man - u - el!
Born to raise the sons of earth; Born to give them sec - ond birth.
Peace on earth and mer - cy mild, God and sin - ners rec - on-ciled!"

Hark! the her - ald an - gels sing, "Glo-ry to the new-born King!"

Text: Charles Wesley (1707—88), cento, alt.
*Tune: **Mendelssohn**, Felix Mendelssohn (1809—47)*

He is born, the Child Di-vine; Play the o-boe, sound the bag-pipes.

He is born, the Child Di-vine; Sing ye all, He is born to-day.

1 Proph-ets from the a-ges past Have fore-told the Sav-ior's com-ing;
2 Ah! How fair is the Ho-ly Child, And how per-fect are His grac-es;
3 In a sta-ble was He born; Straw, a lit-tle, for His cra-dle;
4 King of all for-ev-er-more, Lit-tle In-fant though Thou art,

We for more than four thousand years Have a-wait-ed this joy-ous time.
Ah, how fair is the Ho-ly Child; Oh, how sweet is the Child Di-vine!
In a sta-ble was He born, What a lodg-ing for Christ, the Lord!
King of all for-ev-er-more, Reign in ev-'ry hu-man heart.

Text: *French carol*
Tune: *Il est né le divin enfant (traditional French carol)*
Setting: *Walter Ehret (1917—)*

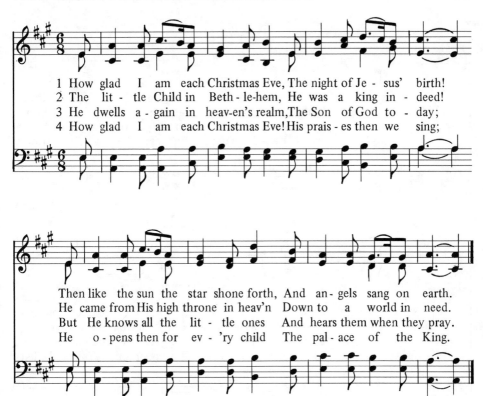

1 How glad I am each Christmas Eve, The night of Je - sus' birth!
2 The lit - tle Child in Beth - le-hem, He was a king in - deed!
3 He dwells a - gain in heav-en's realm, The Son of God to - day;
4 How glad I am each Christmas Eve! His prais - es then we sing;

Then like the sun the star shone forth, And an - gels sang on earth.
He came from His high throne in heav'n Down to a world in need.
But He knows all the lit - tle ones And hears them when they pray.
He o - pens then for ev - 'ry child The pal - ace of the King.

Text: *Marie Wexelsen (1832—1911), cento; trans. Peter Andrew Sveeggen (1881—1959)*
Tune: **Jeg er saa glad**, *Peder Knudsen (1819—63)*

Clap your hands, stamp your feet!
Let your bodies and your voices
        explode with joy.
God is not some human concoction.
He is for real! And He is here!

(Psalm 47)

1 I won-der as I wan-der, out un-der the sky, How
2 When Ma-ry birthed Je-sus, 'twas in a cow's stall, With
3 If Je-sus had want-ed for an-y wee thing, A
4 I won-der as I wan-der, out un-der the sky, How

Je-sus the Sav-ior did come for to die, For poor on-'ry peo-ple like
Wise Men and farmers and shep-herds and all. But high from the heav-ens a
star in the sky or a bird on the wing, Or all of God's an-gels in
Je-sus the Sav-ior did come for to die, For poor on-'ry peo-ple like

you and like I. I won-der as I wan-der, out un-der the sky.
star's light did fall, And the prom-ise of a-ges it then did re-call.
heav'n for to sing, He sure-ly could have it, 'cause He was the King.
you and like I. I won-der as I wan-der, out un-der the sky.

Text: American spiritual
*Tune: **As I wander** (traditional American melody)*
Setting: John Jacob Niles (1892—   )

Joy to the World

1 Joy to the world, the Lord is come! Let earth re-
2 Joy to the earth, the Sav - ior reigns! Let men their
3 No more let sins and sor - rows grow Nor thorns in -
4 He rules the world with truth and grace And makes the

ceive her King; Let ev - 'ry heart pre - pare Him
songs em - ploy, While fields and floods, rocks, hills, and
fest the ground; He comes to make His bless - ings
na - tions prove The glo - ries of His righ - teous -

room And heav'n and na - ture sing, And heav'n and na - ture
plains Re - peat the sound-ing joy, Re - peat the sound-ing
flow Far as the curse is found, Far as the curse is
ness And won-ders of His love, And won-ders of His

sing, And heav'n, and heav'n and na - ture sing.
joy, Re - peat, re - peat the sound-ing joy.
found, Far as, far as the curse is found.
love, And won - ders, won - ders of His love.

Text: Isaac Watts (1674—1748), alt.
Tune: **Antioch**
Setting: Lowell Mason (1792—1872)

1 Let the earth now praise the Lord, Who hath tru - ly kept His word And the sin - ners' Help and Friend Now at last to us doth send.

2 What the fa - thers most de - sired, What the proph - ets' heart in - spired, What they longed for man - y a year, Stands ful - filled in glo - ry here.

3 As Thy com - ing was in peace, Qui - et, full of gen - tle - ness, Let the same mind dwell in me That was ev - er found in Thee.

4 And when Thou dost come a - gain As a glo - rious King to reign, I with joy may see Thy face, Free - ly ran - somed by Thy grace.

Text: Heinrich Held (1620--59), cento; trans. Catherine Winkworth (1827—78)
Tune: **Nun komm, der Heiden Heiland** (Geystliche gesangk Buchleyn, *Wittenberg, 1524*), adapted
Setting: Jan Bender (1909—   )

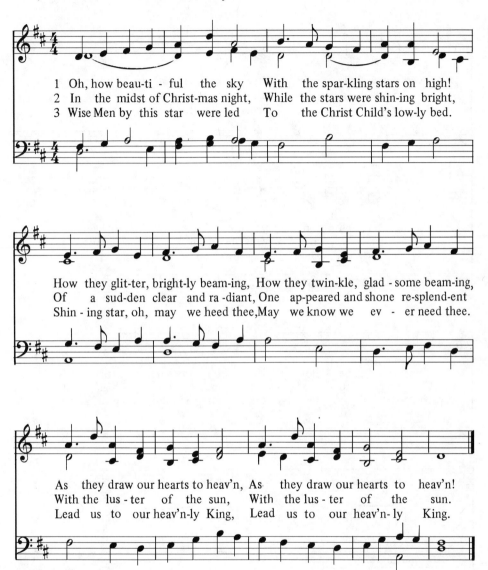

1 Oh, how beau-ti - ful the sky With the spar-kling stars on high!
2 In the midst of Christ-mas night, While the stars were shin-ing bright,
3 Wise Men by this star were led To the Christ Child's low-ly bed.

How they glit-ter, bright-ly beam-ing, How they twin-kle, glad - some beam-ing,
Of a sud-den clear and ra -diant, One ap-peared and shone re-splend-ent
Shin - ing star, oh, may we heed thee, May we know we ev - er need thee.

As they draw our hearts to heav'n, As they draw our hearts to heav'n!
With the lus - ter of the sun, With the lus - ter of the sun.
Lead us to our heav'n-ly King, Lead us to our heav'n- ly King.

Text: Nicolai F.S. Grundtvig (1783—1872), cento; trans. Ingebret Dorrum (1877—1952)
Tune: Dejlig er den himmel blaa (Danish folk carol)
Setting: Healey Willan (1880—1968)

1 Oh, come, all ye faith-ful, joy-ful and tri-um-phant; Oh,
2 Sing, choirs of an-gels, sing in ex-ul-ta-tion;
3 Yea, Lord, we greet Thee, born this hap-py morn-ing;

come ye, oh, come ye to Beth-le-hem;
Sing, all ye cit-i-zens of heav'n a-bove:
Je-sus, to Thee be glo-ry giv'n;

Come and be-hold Him born the King of an-gels.
Glo-ry to God in the high-est! Oh,
Word of the Fa-ther, now in flesh ap-pear-ing!

come, let us a-dore Him; Oh, come, let us a-dore Him; Oh,

come, let us a-dore Him, Christ the Lord!

Text: Ascr. John Francis Wade (c. 1711—86), cento; trans. Frederick Oakley (1802—80), alt.
Tune: *Adeste fideles* (John F. Wade's Cantus Diversi, 1751)
Setting: Richard Hillert (1923—   )

1 Let all to-geth-er praise our God Be - fore His glo-rious
2 The Fa - ther sends Him from His throne To be an in - fant
3 With - in an earth-born form He hides His all - cre - at - ing
4 He un - der-takes a great ex - change, Puts on our hu - man

throne; To - day He o - pens heav'n a - gain To
small And lie here poor - ly man - gered now In
light; To serve us all He hum - bly cloaks The
frame And in re - turn gives us His realm, His

give us His own Son, To give us His own Son.
this cold, dis-mal stall, In this cold, dis-mal stall.
splen-dor of His might, The splen-dor of His might.
glo - ry, and His name, His glo - ry, and His name. A - men.

5 He is a servant, I a lord:
How great a mystery!
How strong the tender Christ Child's love!
No truer friend than He.

6 He is the Key and He the Door
To blessed Paradise;
The angel bars the way no more;
To God our praises rise.

7 Your grace in lowliness revealed,
Lord Jesus, we adore,
And praise to God the Father yield
And Spirit evermore;
We praise You evermore.

Text: Nikolaus Herman (c. 1480—1561); trans. F. Samuel Janzow (1913—   )
Tune: **Lobt Gott, ihr Christen,** *Nikolaus Herman (c. 1480—1561)*

Oh, How Joyfully, Oh, How Merrily

1 Oh, how joy-ful-ly, Oh, how mer-ri-ly Christ-mas
2 Oh, how joy-ful-ly, Oh, how mer-ri-ly Christ-mas
3 Oh, how joy-ful-ly, Oh, how mer-ri-ly Christ-mas

comes with its grace di - vine! Grace a-gain is beam-ing, Christ the world re-
comes with its peace di - vine! Peace on earth is reign-ing, Christ our peace re-
comes with its life di - vine! An - gels high in glo - ry Chant the Christmas

deem - ing:
gain - ing: Hail, ye Chris-tians, hail the joy-ous Christ-mas - time!
sto - ry:

Text: Johannes Daniel Falk (1768—1826); trans. William M. Czamanske (1873—1964)
Tune: *Sicilian Mariners* (traditional Sicilian melody, 18th century)

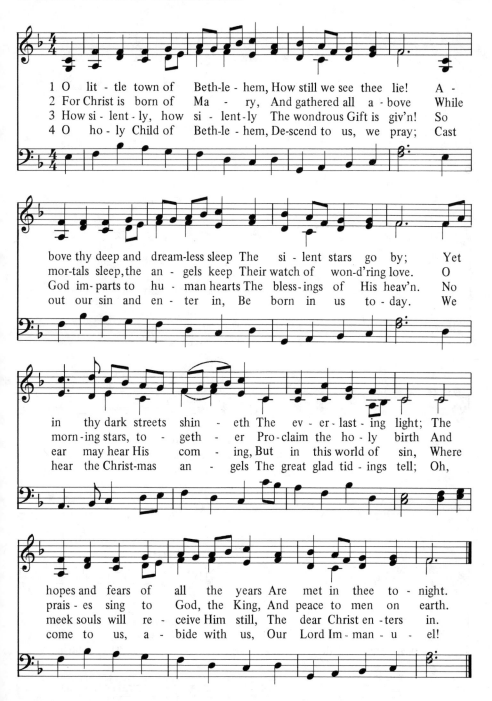

1 O lit - tle town of Beth-le - hem, How still we see thee lie! A -
2 For Christ is born of Ma - ry, And gathered all a - bove While
3 How si - lent - ly, how si - lent-ly The wondrous Gift is giv'n! So
4 O ho - ly Child of Beth-le - hem, De-scend to us, we pray; Cast

bove thy deep and dream-less sleep The si - lent stars go by; Yet
mor-tals sleep, the an - gels keep Their watch of won-d'ring love. O
God im- parts to hu - man hearts The bless-ings of His heav'n. No
out our sin and en - ter in, Be born in us to - day. We

in thy dark streets shin - eth The ev - er-last - ing light; The
morn-ing stars, to - geth - er Pro-claim the ho - ly birth And
ear may hear His com - ing, But in this world of sin, Where
hear the Christ-mas an - gels The great glad tid - ings tell; Oh,

hopes and fears of all the years Are met in thee to - night.
prais - es sing to God, the King, And peace to men on earth.
meek souls will re - ceive Him still, The dear Christ en -ters in.
come to us, a - bide with us, Our Lord Im - man - u - el!

Text: Phillips Brooks (1835—93), cento
Tune: Forest Green (traditional English tune)
Setting: Harmonized by Ralph Vaughan Williams (1872—1958)

1 Si - lent night! Ho - ly night! All is calm,
2 Si - lent night! Ho - ly night! Shep - herds quake
3 Si - lent night! Ho - ly night! Son of God,

all is bright Round yon Vir - gin Moth - er and Child.
at the sight; Glo - ries stream from heav - en a - far,
love's pure light Ra - diant beams from Thy ho- ly face,

Ho - ly In - fant, so ten - der and mild, Sleep in
Heav'n - ly hosts sing, Al - le - lu - ia, Christ, the
With the dawn of re - deem - ing grace, Je - sus,

heav - en - ly peace, Sleep in heav - en - ly peace.
Sav - ior, is born! Christ, the Sav - ior, is born!
Lord, at Thy birth, Je - sus, Lord, at Thy birth.

Text: Joseph Mohr (1792—1848), cento; trans. John Freeman Young (1820—85), alt.
Tune: *Stille Nacht*, Franz Gruber (1787—1863)

1 What child is this, who, laid to rest, On Ma-ry's lap is sleep-ing?
2 Why lies He in such mean es-tate Where ox and ass are feed-ing?
3 So bring Him in-cense, gold, and myrrh, Come, peas-ant, king, to own Him.

Whom an-gels greet with an-thems sweet While shepherds watch are keep-ing?
Good Chris-tian, fear; for sin-ners here The si-lent Word is plead-ing.
The King of kings sal-va-tion brings; Let lov-ing hearts en-throne Him.

This, this is Christ the King, Whom shepherds guard and an-gels sing:
Nails, spear shall pierce Him through, The cross be born for me, for you:
Raise, raise the song on high, The Vir-gin sings her lul-la-by:

Haste, haste to bring Him laud, The Babe, the Son of Ma-ry!
Hail, hail the Word made flesh, The Babe, the Son of Ma-ry!
Joy, joy, for Christ is born, The Babe, the Son of Ma-ry!

Text: *William Chatterton Dix (1837—98)*
Tune: **Greensleeves** *(16th-century English ballad)*

1 O   God,   our   Help   in   a   -   ges   past,   Our
2 Un - der   the   shad - ow   of   Your   throne   Your
3 Be - fore   the   hills   in   or - der   stood   Or

Hope   for   years   to   come,   Our   Shel - ter   from the
saints have   dwelt   se -   cure;   Suf - fi - cient   is Your
earth   re - ceived   her   frame,   From   ev - er - last - ing

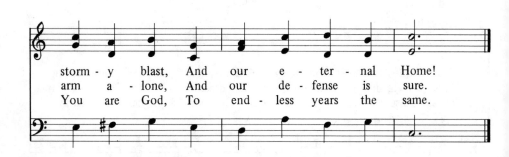

storm - y   blast,   And   our   e -   ter - nal   Home!
arm   a -   lone,   And   our   de - fense   is   sure.
You   are   God,   To   end - less   years   the   same.

4 A thousand ages in Your sight
   Are like an evening gone,
   Short as the watch that ends the night
   Before the rising sun.

5 O God, our Help in ages past,
   Our Hope for years to come,
   Remain our Guard while troubles last
   And our eternal Home!

Text: Isaac Watts (1674—1748), cento, alt.
Tune: St. Anne, William Croft (1678—1727)

As with Gladness Men of Old

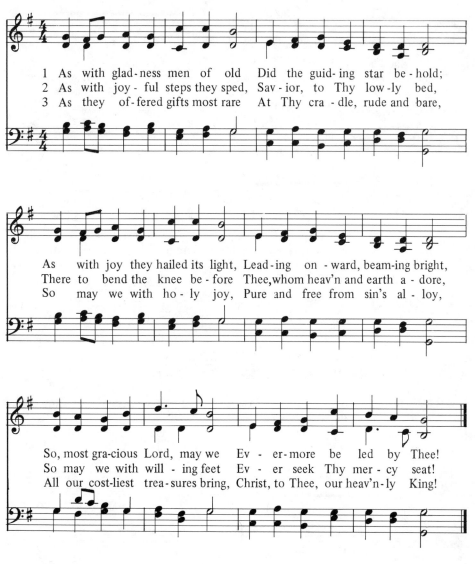

1 As with glad-ness men of old Did the guid-ing star be-hold;
2 As with joy-ful steps they sped, Sav-ior, to Thy low-ly bed,
3 As they of-fered gifts most rare At Thy cra-dle, rude and bare,

As with joy they hailed its light, Lead-ing on-ward, beam-ing bright,
There to bend the knee be-fore Thee, whom heav'n and earth a-dore,
So may we with ho-ly joy, Pure and free from sin's al-loy,

So, most gra-cious Lord, may we Ev-er-more be led by Thee!
So may we with will-ing feet Ev-er seek Thy mer-cy seat!
All our cost-liest trea-sures bring, Christ, to Thee, our heav'n-ly King!

4 Holy Jesus, every day
Keep us in the narrow way;
And, when earthly things are past,
Bring our ransomed souls at last
Where they need no star to guide,
Where no clouds Thy glory hide.

5 In the heavenly country bright
Need they no created light;
Thou its Light, its Joy, its Crown,
Thou its Sun which goes not down.
There forever may we sing
Alleluias to our King!

Text: William Chatterton Dix (1837—98)
Tune: Dix, Konrad Kocher (1786—1872)

1 Of the Fa-ther's love be - got - ten Ere the worlds be - gan to be,
2 Oh, that birth for-ev - er bless-ed When the vir - gin, full of grace,
3 O ye heights of heav'n, a - dore Him; An - gel hosts, His prais-es sing;
4 Christ, to Thee, with God the Fa - ther, And, O Ho - ly Ghost, to Thee

He is Al - pha and O - me - ga, He the Source, the End - ing He
By the Ho - ly Ghost con - ceiv - ing, Bare the Sav - ior of our race,
Pow'rs, do - min-ions, bow be - fore Him And ex - tol our God and King.
Hymn and chant and high thanksgiv- ing And un - end - ing prais-es be,

Of the things that are, that have been, And that fu-ture years
And the Babe, the world's Re - deem - er, First re-vealed His sa -
Let no tongue on earth be si - lent, Ev-'ry voice in con -
Hon- or, glo - ry, and do - min - ion, And e - ter- nal vic -

shall see Ev-er-more and ev - er-more.
cred face Ev-er-more and ev - er-more.
cert ring Ev-er-more and ev - er-more.
to - ry Ev-er-more and ev - er-more. A - men.

Text: *Aurelius Prudentius (348—c.413); st. 4 anonymous; trans. John Mason Neale (1818—66);*
adapted 1859 by Henry W. Baker (1821—77)
Tune: **Divinum mysterium** *(Plainsong, Mode V, 13th century)*

1 What star is this, with beams so bright, More
2 True spake the proph - et from a - far Who
3 The guid - ing star a - bove is bright; With -
4 O Je - sus, while the star of grace Im -

beau - teous than the noon - day light? It shines to her - ald
told the rise of Ja - cob's star, And East - ern sag - es
in them shines a clear - er light And leads them on with
pels on us to seek Thy face, Let not our sloth - ful

forth the King And Gen - tiles to His crib to bring.
with a - maze Up - on the won - drous sign did gaze.
pow'r be - nign To seek the Giv - er of the sign.
hearts re - fuse The guid - ance of Thy light to use.

Text: Charles Coffin (1676—1749); trans. Edward Thring (1821—87), alt.
*Tune: **Puer nobis nascitur** (Musae Sioniae, VI, 1609)*

The
Easter and Pentecost
Cycle

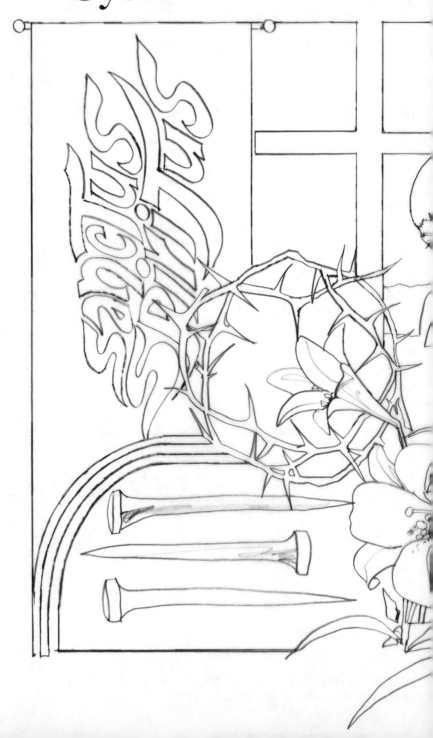

Christ, the Life of All the Living

1 Christ, the Life of all the liv-ing, Christ, the Death of death, our foe,
2 Thou hast suf-fered great af-flic-tion And hast borne it pa-tient-ly,
3 Then, for all that wrought my par-don, For Thy sor-rows deep and sore,

Who, Thy-self for me once giv-ing To the dark-est depths of woe,
Ev-en death by cru-ci-fix-ion, Ful-ly to a-tone for me;
For Thine an-guish in the Gar-den, I will thank Thee ev-er-more,

Thro' Thy suf-f'rings, death, and mer-it I e-ter-nal life in-her-it:
Thou didst choose to be tor-ment-ed That my doom should be pre-vent-ed.
Thank Thee for Thy groan-ing, sigh-ing, For Thy bleed-ing and Thy dy-ing,

Thou-sand, thou-sand thanks shall be, Dear-est Je-sus, un-to Thee.
Thou-sand, thou-sand thanks shall be, Dear-est Je-sus, un-to Thee.
For that last tri-um-phant cry, And shall praise Thee, Lord, on high.

Text: Ernst C. Homburg (1605—81), cento; trans. Catherine Winkworth (1827—78), alt.
*Tune: **Jesu, meines Lebens Leben** (Kirchengesangbuch, Dresden, 1687)*

1 My song is love un-known, My Sav-ior's love to me, Love
2 He came from His blest throne, Sal-va-tion to be-stow; But
3 Some-times they strew His way And His sweet prais-es sing, Re -
4 Why, what has my Lord done? What makes this rage and spite? He

to the love-less shown That they might love - ly be. Oh,
men made strange, and none The longed-for Christ would know. But
sound-ing all the day Ho-san-nas to their King. Then
made the lame to run, He gave the blind their sight. Sweet

who am I That for my sake The Lord should take Frail flesh and die?
oh, my Friend, My Friend in-deed, Who at my need His life did spend!
"Cru-ci-fy!" Is all their breath, And for His death They thirst and cry.
in - ju-ries! Yet they at these Them-selves dis-please And 'gainst Him rise.

5 They rise and needs will have
My dear Lord made away;
A murderer they save,
The Prince of Life they slay.
Yet cheerful He
To suffering goes
That He His foes
From thence might free.

6 Here might I stay and sing
No story so divine;
Never was love, dear King,
Never was grief like Thine!
This is my Friend,
In whose sweet praise
I all my days
Could gladly spend.

Text: *Samuel Crossman (c. 1624--83), cento*
Tune: **Love unknown,** *John Ireland (1879--1962)*
Setting: *Richard Hillert (1923—)*

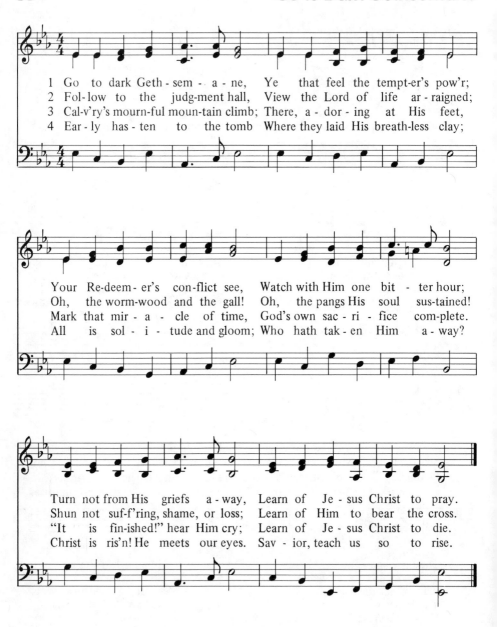

1 Go to dark Geth-sem-a-ne, Ye that feel the tempt-er's pow'r;
2 Fol-low to the judg-ment hall, View the Lord of life ar-raigned;
3 Cal-v'ry's mourn-ful moun-tain climb; There, a-dor-ing at His feet,
4 Ear-ly has-ten to the tomb Where they laid His breath-less clay;

Your Re-deem-er's con-flict see, Watch with Him one bit-ter hour;
Oh, the worm-wood and the gall! Oh, the pangs His soul sus-tained!
Mark that mir-a-cle of time, God's own sac-ri-fice com-plete.
All is sol-i-tude and gloom; Who hath tak-en Him a-way?

Turn not from His griefs a-way, Learn of Je-sus Christ to pray.
Shun not suf-f'ring, shame, or loss; Learn of Him to bear the cross.
"It is fin-ished!" hear Him cry; Learn of Je-sus Christ to die.
Christ is ris'n! He meets our eyes. Sav-ior, teach us so to rise.

Text: James Montgomery (1771—1854)
*Tune: **Gethsemane**, Richard Redhead (1820—1901)*

(Sung to *Gethsemane*, #35)

1 By Your birth and by Your tears,
By Your human griefs and fears,
By Your conflict in the hour
Of the subtle tempter's power:
Savior, You have freed me too;
Help me to forgive as You.

2 By Your lonely hour of prayer,
By Your fearful conflict there,
By Your cross and dying cries,
By Your one great sacrifice:
Savior, You have freed me too;
Help me to forgive as You.

3 By Your triumph o'er the grave,
By Your power the lost to save,
From Your Father's heavenly throne,
You have said I'm not alone:
Savior, You have freed me too;
Help me to forgive as You.

Text: Robert Grant (1785—1838), alt.
*Tune: **Gethsemane**, Richard Redhead (1820—1901)*

Everyone must eventually face up to You,
        and it must be with all
            of his sins and shortcomings.
But anyone who comes in sorrow and repentance
        shall find You merciful and gracious.
You shall forgive his sins,
            and You shall reconcile him to Your kingdom
            and fill his heart with Your love and joy.
                                    (Psalm 65)

1 What won-drous love is this, O my soul, O my
2 To God and to the Lamb I will sing, I will
3 And when from death I'm free, I'll sing on, I'll sing

soul, What won-drous love is this, O my soul;
sing, To God and to the Lamb I will sing,
on, And when from death I'm free, I'll sing on!

What won-drous love is this That caused the Lord of
To God and to the Lamb, Who is the great I
And when from death I'm free, I'll sing and joy-ful

bliss To bear the dread-ful curse for my soul, for my
Am, While mil-lions join the theme, I will sing, I will
be, And through e - ter - ni - ty I'll sing on, I'll sing

soul, To   bear the dread-ful curse for my soul.
sing, While mil - lions join the theme, I will sing.
on,   And through e - ter - ni - ty I'll sing on!

Text: *Traditional American folk hymn (J. Mercer,* Cluster of Spiritual Songs, *1836)*
Tune: **Wondrous love** (Southern Harmony, *1835)*

O God, I am crying for help!
This is not a pious exclamation;
     I mean it! I'm desperate!
If You don't listen, I'll go down the drain!

Don't let me float downstream
     with those who ignore You.
I know they shall go over the edge if they persist
     in their course of rebelliousness and indifference.
Reach forth, O God,
     and snatch me out of this overpowering current
          lest I perish with them.

I thank You, O God.
You have heard my agonizing cry.
I called for You, and You responded.
You are my Hope and my Salvation.
I will sing Your praises forever.

And thus the Lord is the Hope and Salvation
     of all who trust in Him.
Stay close to those who struggle, O God;
     never let them go.

(Psalm 28)

38

There Is a Green Hill Far Away

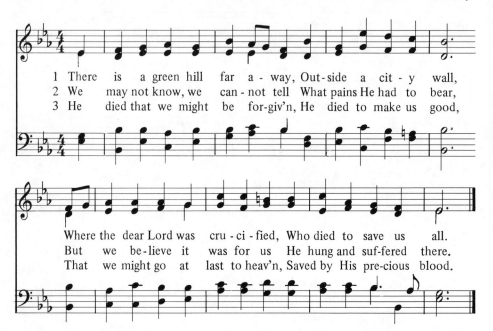

1 There is a green hill far a-way, Out-side a cit-y wall,
2 We may not know, we can-not tell What pains He had to bear,
3 He died that we might be for-giv'n, He died to make us good,

Where the dear Lord was cru-ci-fied, Who died to save us all.
But we be-lieve it was for us He hung and suf-fered there.
That we might go at last to heav'n, Saved by His pre-cious blood.

4 There was no other good enough
To pay the price of sin,
He only could unlock the gate
Of heaven and let us in.

5 Oh, dearly, dearly has He loved!
And we must love Him too
And trust in His redeeming blood
And try His works to do.

Text: Cecil Francis Alexander (1818--95), alt.
*Tune: **Horsley**, William Horsley (1774--1858)*

39

Were You There

D chords: Capo 1

| (D) | (D) | | (A) | (F#m) | (Bm)(G) | (D) | (D) |
| Eb | Eb | | Bb | Gm | Cm Ab | Eb | Eb |

1 Were you there when they cru - ci-fied my Lord? Were you
2 Were you there when they nailed Him to the tree? Were you
3 Were you there when they laid Him in the tomb? Were you
4 Were you there when He rose up from the dead? Were you

there when they cru - ci - fied my Lord? Oh! _____
there when they nailed Him to the tree? Oh! _____
there when they laid Him in the tomb? Oh! _____
there when He rose up from the dead? Oh! _____

Some-times it caus - es me to trem - ble, trem - ble, trem - ble. ____
Some-times it caus - es me to trem - ble, trem - ble, trem - ble. ____
Some-times it caus - es me to trem - ble, trem - ble, trem - ble. ____
Some-times it caus - es me to trem - ble, trem - ble, trem - ble. ____

Were you there when they cru - ci - fied my Lord?
Were you there when they nailed Him to the tree?
Were you there when they laid Him in the tomb?
Were you there when He rose up from the dead?

Text: *American spiritual*
Tune: **Were you there** *(American spiritual)*

The King of Glo - ry comes, the na - tion re - joic - es;

O - pen the gates be - fore Him, lift up your voic - es.

1 Who is the King of Glo - ry; how shall we call Him?
2 In all of Gal - i - lee, in cit - y or vil - lage,
3 Sing then of Da - vid's son, our Sav - ior and Broth - er;

He is Em - man - u - el, the Prom - ised of a - ges.
He goes a - mong His peo - ple cur - ing their ill - ness.
In all of Gal - i - lee was nev - er an - oth - er.

4 He gave His life for us, the Lamb of salvation,
   He took upon Himself the sins of the nation.
   Refrain

5 He conquered sin and death, He truly has risen,
   And He will share with us His heavenly vision.
   Refrain

Text: Willard F. Jabusch (1930—)
Tune: The King of Glory (Israeli folksong)
Setting: Charles Ore (1936—)

1 All glory laud, and hon - or To Thee, Re-deem-er, King, To whom the lips of chil - dren Made sweet ho-san-nas ring. Thou art the King of Is - rael, Thou Da-vid's roy - al Son, Who in the Lord's name com - est, The King and Bless-ed One.

2 All glory, laud, and hon - or To Thee, Re-deem-er, King, To whom the lips of chil - dren Made sweet ho-san-nas ring. The com-pa-ny of an - gels Are prais-ing Thee on high, And mor - tal men and all things Cre - at - ed make re - ply.

3 All glory, laud, and hon - or To Thee, Re-deem-er, King, To whom the lips of chil - dren Made sweet ho-san-nas ring. The peo - ple of the He - brews With palms be - fore Thee went; Our praise and prayer and an - thems Be - fore Thee we pre - sent.

4 All glory, laud, and honor
To Thee, Redeemer, King,
To whom the lips of children
Made sweet hosannas ring.
To Thee, before Thy Passion,
They sang their hymns of praise;
To Thee, now high exalted,
Our melody we raise.

5 All glory, laud, and honor
To Thee, Redeemer, King,
To whom the lips of children
Made sweet hosannas ring.
Thou didst accept their praises;
Accept the prayers we bring,
Who in all good delightest,
Thou good and gracious King.

Text: Theodulph of Orleans (? —821); trans. John Mason Neale (1818—66), alt.
Tune: Valet will ich dir geben, Melchior Teschner (1584—1635)

Refrain

Ho - san - na, hal - le - lu - jah!   Sing we loud and clear.

Ho - san - na, hal - le - lu - jah!   Je - sus Christ is near.

With an-cient psalms and new - grown palms   Praise Him on His way.

Ho - san - na, hal - le - lu - jah!   Christ, our Lord, is here.

1 This day in spring the streets will ring with voic-es sweet and lyr - i - cal
2 King Da-vid's Son now rides up - on   a mule, of beasts the low-li - est;
3 How ver - y odd the Son of God must do things that would weary us.

Text: Richard K. Avery (1934—) and Donald S. Marsh (1923—)
Tune: *Hosanna, hallelujah!* Richard K. Avery (1934—) and Donald S. Marsh (1923—)

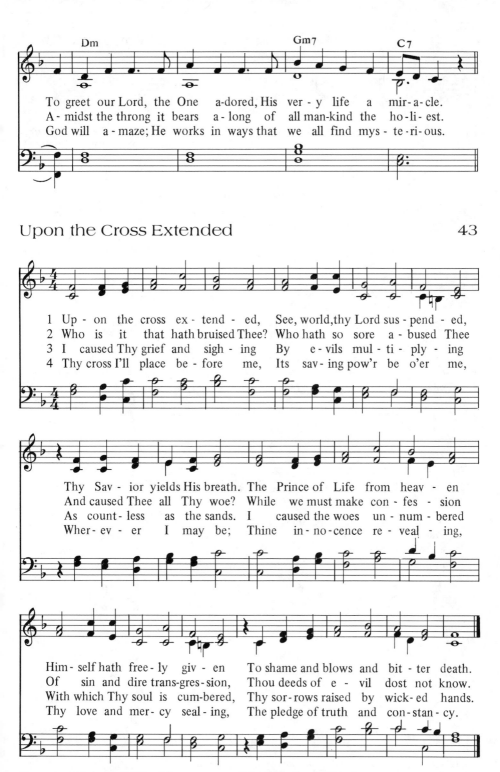

To greet our Lord, the One a-dored, His ver-y life a mir-a-cle.
A-midst the throng it bears a-long of all man-kind the ho-li-est.
God will a-maze; He works in ways that we all find mys-te-ri-ous.

Upon the Cross Extended 43

1 Up-on the cross ex-tend-ed, See, world, thy Lord sus-pend-ed,
2 Who is it that hath bruised Thee? Who hath so sore a-bused Thee
3 I caused Thy grief and sigh-ing By e-vils mul-ti-ply-ing
4 Thy cross I'll place be-fore me, Its sav-ing pow'r be o'er me,

Thy Sav-ior yields His breath. The Prince of Life from heav-en
And caused Thee all Thy woe? While we must make con-fes-sion
As count-less as the sands. I caused the woes un-num-bered
Wher-ev-er I may be; Thine in-no-cence re-veal-ing,

Him-self hath free-ly giv-en To shame and blows and bit-ter death.
Of sin and dire trans-gres-sion, Thou deeds of e-vil dost not know.
With which Thy soul is cum-bered, Thy sor-rows raised by wick-ed hands.
Thy love and mer-cy seal-ing, The pledge of truth and con-stan-cy.

Text: *Paul Gerhardt (1607--76), cento; trans. John Kelly (? --1890), alt.*
Tune: ***O Welt, ich muss dich lassen,*** *Heinrich Isaak (c.1455--1517)*

When I Survey the Wondrous Cross

1 When I sur - vey the won - drous cross On which the
2 For - bid it, Lord, that I should boast Save in the
3 See, from His head, His hands, His feet Sor - row and
4 Were the whole realm of na - ture mine, That were a

Prince of Glo - ry died, My rich - est gain I
death of Christ, my God; All the vain things that
love flow min - gled down. Did e'er such love and
trib - ute far too small; Love so a - maz - ing,

count but loss And pour con - tempt on all my pride.
charm me most, I sac - ri - fice them to His blood.
sor - row meet Or thorns com - pose so rich a crown?
so di - vine, De - mands my soul, my life, my all.

Text: Isaac Watts (1674—1748), abbr. and alt.
Tune: **Hamburg**
Setting: Lowell Mason (1792—1872)

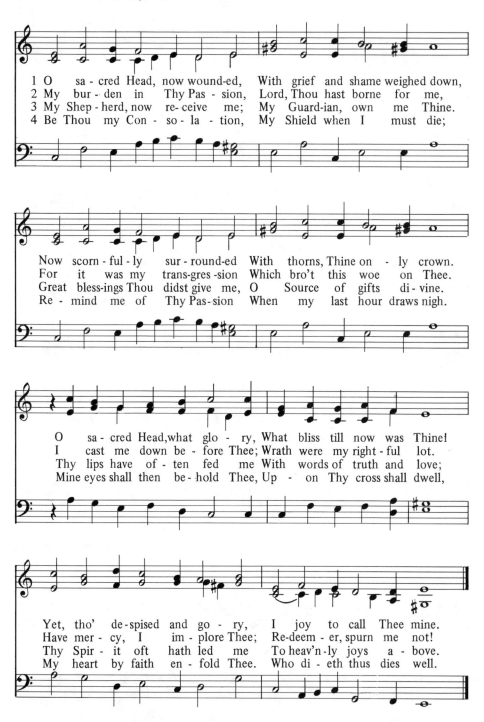

1 O sa - cred Head, now wound-ed, With grief and shame weighed down,
2 My bur - den in Thy Pas - sion, Lord, Thou hast borne for me,
3 My Shep - herd, now re - ceive me; My Guard-ian, own me Thine.
4 Be Thou my Con - so - la - tion, My Shield when I must die;

Now scorn - ful - ly sur - round-ed With thorns, Thine on - ly crown.
For it was my trans-gres -sion Which bro't this woe on Thee.
Great bless-ings Thou didst give me, O Source of gifts di - vine.
Re - mind me of Thy Pas-sion When my last hour draws nigh.

O sa - cred Head, what glo - ry, What bliss till now was Thine!
I cast me down be - fore Thee; Wrath were my right - ful lot.
Thy lips have of - ten fed me With words of truth and love;
Mine eyes shall then be - hold Thee, Up - on Thy cross shall dwell,

Yet, tho' de - spised and go - ry, I joy to call Thee mine.
Have mer - cy, I im - plore Thee; Re-deem - er, spurn me not!
Thy Spir - it oft hath led me To heav'n - ly joys a - bove.
My heart by faith en - fold Thee. Who di - eth thus dies well.

Text: Ascr. to St. Bernard of Clairvaux (1091—1153); Paul Gerhardt (1607—76); trans. composite
*Tune: **Herzlich tut mich verlangen**, Hans Leo Hassler (1564—1612)*

This Joyful Eastertide

1 This joy - ful Eas-ter-tide, A - way with sin and sor -
2 Death's flood has lost its chill Since Je - sus crossed the riv -
3 My flesh in hope shall rest And for a sea - son slum -

- row! My Love, the Cru-ci-fied, Has sprung to life this mor -
- er. Lov- er of souls, from ill My pass - ing soul de-liv -
- ber Till trump from east to west Shall wake the dead in num -

Refrain

- row:
- er: Had Christ, who once was slain, Not burst His three-day pris-on,
- ber:

Our faith had been in vain; But now has Christ a - ris - en, a -

ris - en, a - ris - en; But now has Christ a - ris - en!

Text: George R. Woodward (1848—1934)
Tune: **Vruechten** (17th-century Dutch tune)
Setting: Paul Bunjes (1914—)

1 Je - sus Christ is ris'n to - day, Al - le - lu - ia!
2 Hymns of praise, then, let us sing, Al - le - lu - ia!
3 But the pains which He en - dured, Al - le - lu - ia!
4 Sing we to our God a - bove, Al - le - lu - ia!

Our tri - um-phant ho - ly day, Al - le - lu - ia!
Un - to Christ, our heav'n-ly King, Al - le - lu - ia!
Our sal - va - tion have pro - cured. Al - le - lu - ia!
Praise e - ter - nal as His love: Al - le - lu - ia!

Who did once up - on the cross, Al - le - lu - ia!
Who en - dured the cross and grave, Al - le - lu - ia!
Now a - bove the sky He's King, Al - le - lu - ia!
Praise Him, all ye heav'n - ly host, Al - le - lu - ia!

Suf - fer to re - deem our loss. Al - le - lu - ia!
Sin - ners to re - deem and save. Al - le - lu - ia!
Where the an - gels ev - er sing. Al - le - lu - ia!
Fa - ther, Son, and Ho - ly Ghost. Al - le - lu - ia! A - men.

Text: Bohemian Latin carol, 14th century; st. 1 trans. Lyra Davidica, *1708, alt.; st. 2 and 3*
trans. Arnold's Compleat Psalmodist, *1749; st. 4, Charles Wesley (1707—88), alt.*
Tune: Easter hymn (Lyra Davidica, 1708)

1 I know that my Re - deem - er lives;
What com-fort this sweet sen - tence gives! He lives, He lives, who once was dead; He lives, my ev - er - liv - ing Head.

2 He lives tri - um - phant from the grave, He lives e - ter - nal - ly to save, He lives all - glo - rious in the sky, He lives ex - alt - ed there on high.

3 He lives to si - lence all my fears, He lives to wipe a - way my tears, He lives to calm my trou - bled heart, He lives all bless - ings to im - part.

4 He lives, my kind, wise, heavenly Friend,
He lives and loves me to the end;
He lives and grants me daily breath;
He lives, and I shall conquer death.

5 He lives, all glory to His name!
He lives, my Jesus, still the same.
Oh, the sweet joy this sentence gives:
"I know that my Redeemer lives!"

Text: Samuel Medley (1738—99), cento
Tune: **Duke Street,** *John Hatton (†1793)*

1 At the Lamb's high feast we sing Praise to our vic-
2 Might-y Vic-tim from the sky, Hell's fierce pow'rs be-
3 Eas-ter tri-umph, Eas-ter joy, Sin a-lone can
4 Hymns of glo-ry, songs of praise, Fa-ther, un-to

to-rious King, Who has washed us in the tide
neath Thee lie; Thou hast con-quered in the fight,
this de-stroy; From sin's pow'r do Thou set free
Thee we raise: Ris-en Lord, all praise to Thee

Flow-ing from His pierc-ed side. Al-le-lu-ia!
Thou hast brought us life and light. Al-le-lu-ia!
Souls new-born, O Lord, in Thee. Al-le-lu-ia!
With the Spir-it ev-er be. Al-le-lu-ia! A-men.

Text: 17th-century Office hymn; trans. Robert Campbell (1814--68), cento, alt.
*Tune: **Sonne der Gerechtigkeit** (15th-century tune; Bohemian Brethren, 1566)*
Setting: Jan Bender (1909—   )

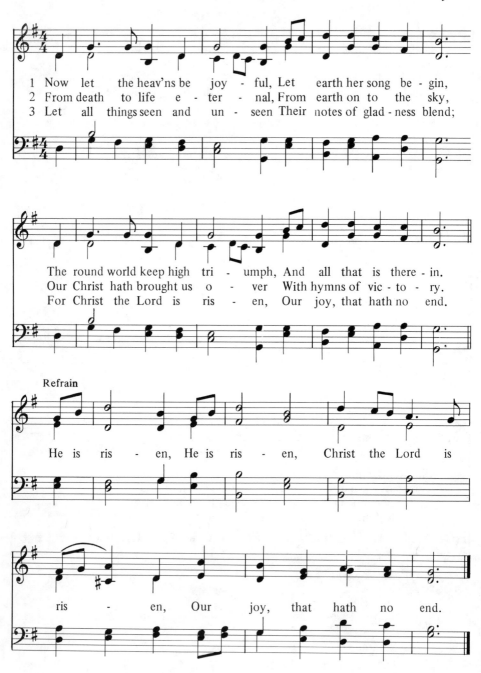

1 Now let the heav'ns be joy - ful, Let earth her song be - gin,
2 From death to life e - ter - nal, From earth on to the sky,
3 Let all things seen and un - seen Their notes of glad - ness blend;

The round world keep high tri - umph, And all that is there - in.
Our Christ hath brought us o - ver With hymns of vic - to - ry.
For Christ the Lord is ris - en, Our joy, that hath no end.

Refrain

He is ris - en, He is ris - en, Christ the Lord is

ris - en, Our joy, that hath no end.

Text: John of Damascus (c. 696—c. 754), cento; trans. John Mason Neale (1818–66), alt.
Tune: Provençal carol
Setting: Healey Willan (1880—1968)

1 Now the green blade ris - eth from the bur - ied grain.
2 In the grave they laid Him, Love whom men had slain,
3 Forth He came at Eas - ter, like the ris - en grain,
4 When our hearts are win - try, griev - ing, or in pain,

Wheat that in dark earth man - y days has lain;
Think - ing that nev - er He would wake a - gain,
He that for three days in the grave had lain.
Thy touch can call us back to life a - gain,

Love lives a - gain, that with the dead has been:
Laid in the earth like grain that sleeps un - seen:
Quick from the dead my ris - en Lord is seen:
Fields of our hearts that dead and bare have been:

Love is come a - gain like wheat that spring - eth green.

Text: J.M.C. Crum (1872—1958)
Tune: Noël nouvelet (traditional French carol)
Setting: Martin Shaw (1875—1958)

1 Good Chris - tian men, re - joice and sing! Now is the
2 The Lord of life is ris'n for aye; Bring flow'rs of
3 Praise we in songs of vic - to - ry That Love, that
4 Thy name we bless, O ris - en Lord, And sing to -

tri - umph of our King! To all the world glad news we bring:
song to strew His way; Let all man - kind re - joice and say:
Life which can - not die, And sing with hearts up - lift - ed high:
day with one ac - cord The life laid down, the Life re - stored:

Al - le - lu - ia!   Al - le - lu - ia!   Al - le - lu - ia!

Text: Cyril A. Alington (1872—1955)
*Tune: **Gelobt sei Gott**, Melchior Vulpius (c. 1570—1615)*
Setting: Richard Hillert (1923—)

O Sons and Daughters of the King

(Sung to *Gelobt sei Gott,* #52)

1 O sons and daughters of the King,
Whom heavenly hosts in glory sing,
Today the grave has lost its sting. Alleluia!

2 That Easter morn, at break of day,
The faithful women went their way
To seek the tomb where Jesus lay. Alleluia!

3 An angel clad in white they see,
Who sat and spoke unto the three,
"Your Lord is gone to Galilee." Alleluia!

4 That night the apostles met in fear;
Amidst them came their Lord most dear
And said, "Peace be unto you here." Alleluia!

*5 When Thomas afterwards had heard
That Jesus had fulfilled His word,
He doubted if it were the Lord. Alleluia!

*6 "Thomas, behold My side," said He,
"My hands, My feet, My body see,
And doubt not, but believe in Me." Alleluia!

*7 No longer Thomas then denied;
He saw the hands, the feet, the side;
"You are my Lord and God," he cried. Alleluia!

*8 Blessèd are they that have not seen
And yet whose faith has constant been;
In life eternal they shall reign. Alleluia!

9 On this most holy day of days
To God your hearts and voices raise
In laud and jubilee and praise. Alleluia!

* Sing on days the Thomas account is used.

Text: *Text: Jean Tisserand († 1494), cento; trans. John Mason Neale (1818—66), alt.*
*Tune: **Gelobt sei Gott,** Melchior Vulpius (c. 1570- -1615)*
Setting: Richard Hillert (1923--   )

Christ Is Arisen

Christ is a - ris - en From the grave's dark pris - on. We now re - joice

with glad - ness; Christ will end all sad - ness. Lord, have mer - cy.

All our hopes were end - ed Had Je - sus not as - cend - ed

From the grave tri - um - phant - ly. For this, Lord Christ, we wor - ship Thee.

Lord, have mer - cy. Hal - le - lu - jah! Hal - le -

lu - jah! Hal - le - lu - jah! We now re - joice with

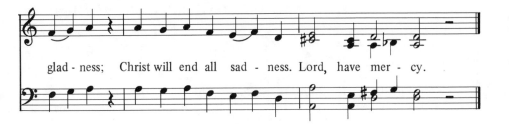

glad - ness; Christ will end all sad - ness. Lord, have mer - cy.

Text: *12th-century anonymous German text; trans. W. Gustave Polack (1890—1950)*
Tune: **Christ ist erstanden** (Geistliche Lieder, *Erfurt, 1531)*

Christ the Lord Is Risen Today, Sons 55

1 "Christ the Lord is ris'n to - day," Sons of men and an - gels say.
2 Lives a - gain our glo - rious King; Where, O death, is now thy sting?
3 Hail the Lord of earth and heav'n! Praise to Thee by both be giv'n!

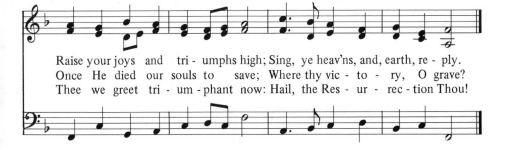

Raise your joys and tri - umphs high; Sing, ye heav'ns, and, earth, re - ply.
Once He died our souls to save; Where thy vic - to - ry, O grave?
Thee we greet tri - um - phant now: Hail, the Res - ur - rec - tion Thou!

Text: *Charles Wesley (1707—88), cento*
Tune: **Orientis partibus** *(medieval French melody)*

1 Christ the Lord is ris'n to - day; Al - le - lu - ia!
2 For the sheep the Lamb hath bled, Al - le - lu - ia!
3 Chris-tians, on this hap - py day, Al - le - lu - ia!

Chris-tians, haste your vows to pay; Al - le - lu - ia!
Sin - less in the sin - ners' stead. Al - le - lu - ia!
Haste with joy your vows to pay. Al - le - lu - ia!

Of - fer now your prais - es sweet, Al - le - lu - ia!
"Christ is ris'n," to - day we cry; Al - le - lu - ia!
"Christ is ris'n," to - day we cry; Al - le - lu - ia!

At the Pas - chal Vic - tim's feet. Al - le - lu - ia!
Now He lives no more to die. Al - le - lu - ia!
Now He lives no more to die. Al - le - lu - ia!

Text: Anonymous Latin (c. 1100); trans. Jane E. Leeson (1807—82), cento
*Tune: **Llanfair**, Robert Williams (c. 1781—1821)*
Setting: R. Harold Terry (1925—)

1 We wel-come glad Eas-ter, when Je-sus a-rose And won a great
2 And tell how three Ma-rys came ear-ly that day And there at the
3 And sing of the an-gel who said: "Do not fear! Your Sav-ior has
4 Think now of the prom-ise which Je-sus has giv'n, That he who be -

vic - to - ry o - ver His foes.
tomb found the stone rolled a - way.
ris'n to - day, He is not here." "Then raise your glad voic - es, you
lieves in Him al - so shall live.

chil - dren, and sing, Bring sweet Eas - ter prais - es to Je-sus, our King.

Text: Anonymous
Tune: **St. Denio** *(traditional Welsh tune)*
Setting: Richard Hillert (1923--)

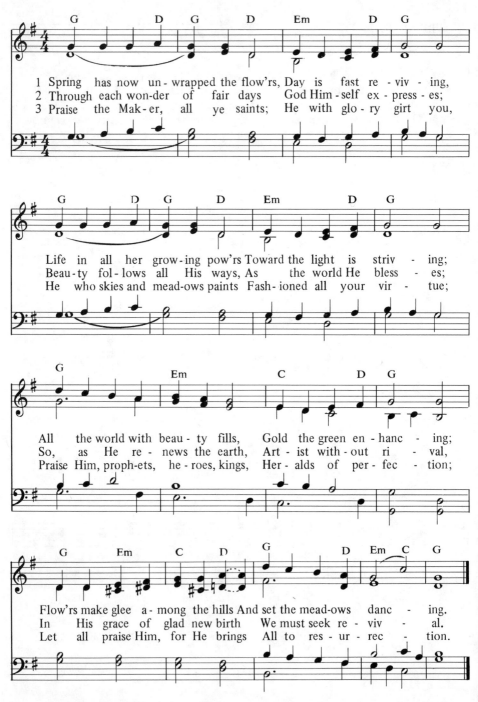

1 Spring has now un-wrapped the flow'rs, Day is fast re-viv-ing,
2 Through each won-der of fair days God Him-self ex-press-es;
3 Praise the Mak-er, all ye saints; He with glo-ry girt you,

Life in all her grow-ing pow'rs Toward the light is striv-ing;
Beau-ty fol-lows all His ways, As the world He bless-es;
He who skies and mead-ows paints Fash-ioned all your vir-tue;

All the world with beau-ty fills, Gold the green en-hanc-ing;
So, as He re-news the earth, Art-ist with-out ri-val,
Praise Him, proph-ets, he-roes, kings, Her-alds of per-fec-tion;

Flow'rs make glee a-mong the hills And set the mead-ows danc-ing.
In His grace of glad new birth We must seek re-viv-al.
Let all praise Him, for He brings All to res-ur-rec-tion.

Text: Piae Cantiones, *1582; trans. Percy Dearmer (1867—1936),* Oxford Book of Carols, *1928*
Tune: **Tempus adest floridum** (Piae Cantiones, *1582*)
Setting: Theodore Beck (1929—   )

Oh, He's King of kings, Oh, He's Lord of lords!

Je - sus Christ, the First and Last, No man works like Him.

1 I know that my Re - deem - er lives,
2 Vic - to - ri - ous at God's right hand, No man works like Him,
3 O sin - ner, if you will be - lieve,

And by His love sweet bless - ings gives,
He calls His saints from ev - 'ry land, No man works like Him.
Grace of the Lord you will re - ceive,

Text: American spiritual
*Tune: **King of kings** (American spiritual)*

1 Re - joice,   the   Lord   is   King!   Your   Lord   and   King   a -
2 Je - sus,   the   Sav - ior,   reigns,   The   God   of   truth   and
3 His   king - dom   can - not   fail,   He   rules   o'er   earth   and
4 Re - joice   in   glo - rious   hope!   Our   Lord   the   Judge   shall

dore!   Re - joice,   give   thanks,   and   sing,   And   tri - umph
love;   When   He   had   purged   our   stains,   He   took   His
heav'n;   The   keys   of   death   and   hell   Are   to   our
come   And   take   His   ser - vants   up   To   their   e -

ev - er - more: Lift   up   your   heart!   Lift
seat   a - bove:
Je - sus   giv'n:
ter - nal   home:

up   your voice! Re- joice! A - gain   I   say,   Re - joice!

Text: *Charles Wesley (1707—88), cento*
Tune: *Darwall's 148th, John Darwall (1731—89)*

1 Draw us to Thee, For then shall we
2 Draw us to Thee, Lord, lov - ing - ly;
3 Draw us to Thee; Oh, grant that we

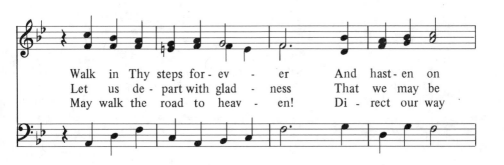

Walk in Thy steps for - ev - er And hast - en on
Let us de - part with glad - ness That we may be
May walk the road to heav - en! Di - rect our way

Where Thou art gone To be with Thee, dear Sav - ior.
For - ev - er free From sor - row, grief, and sad - ness.
Lest we should stray And from Thy paths be driv - en.

4 Draw us to Thee
  That also we
  Thy heavenly bliss inherit
  And ever dwell
  Where sin and hell
  No more can vex our spirit.

5 Draw us to Thee
  Unceasingly,
  Into Thy kingdom take us;
  Let us fore'er
  Thy glory share;
  Thy saints and joint heirs make us.

Text: Friedrich Funcke (1642—99); trans. August Crull (1846—1923)
*Tune: **Ach Gott und Herr** (C. Peter, Andachts–Zymbeln, Freyberg, 1655)*

1 Crown Him with man-y crowns, The Lamb up-on His throne; Hark
2 Crown Him the Lord of Life Who tri-umphed o'er the grave And
3 Crown Him the Lord of Heav'n, En-throned in worlds a-bove, Crown

how the heav'n-ly an-them drowns All mu-sic but its own. A-
rose vic-to-rious in the strife For those He came to save. His
Him the King to whom is giv'n The won-drous name of Love. Crown

wake, my soul, and sing Of Him who died for thee And
glo-ries now we sing Who died and rose on high, Who
Him with man-y crowns As thrones be-fore Him fall; Crown

hail Him as thy match-less King Thro' all e-ter-ni-ty.
died e-ter-nal life to bring And lives that death may die.
Him, ye kings, with man-y crowns, For He is King of all.

Text: Matthew Bridges (1800—94), cento, alt.
Tune: **Diademata**, *George J. Elvey (1816—93)*

Holy Spirit, Ever Dwelling   63

1 Ho - ly Spir-it, ev - er dwell-ing In the ho - liest realms of light;
2 Ho - ly Spir-it, ev - er liv - ing As the church's ver - y life;
3 Ho - ly Spir-it, ev - er work-ing Thro' the church's min - is - try;

Ho - ly Spir - it, ev - er brood-ing O'er a world of gloom and night;
Ho - ly Spir - it, ev - er striv-ing Thro' her in a cease - less strife;
Quick-'ning, strength-'ning, and ab-solv-ing, Set - ting cap-tive sin - ners free;

Ho - ly Spir-it, ev - er rais-ing Sons of earth to thrones on high;
Ho - ly Spir-it, ev - er form-ing In the church the mind of Christ;
Ho - ly Spir-it, ev - er bind-ing Age to age and soul to soul,

Liv - ing, life - im - part-ing Spir-it, Thee we praise and mag-ni - fy.
Thee we praise with end-less wor-ship For Thy fruit and gifts un-priced.
In a fel - low-ship un - end - ing Thee we wor - ship and ex - tol.

Text: Timothy Rees (1874—1939)
*Tune: **In Babilone** (traditional Dutch tune)*
Setting: Carl Schalk (1929—   )

1 O Ho-ly Spir-it, en-ter in And in our hearts Thy work be-
2 Give to Thy Word im-press-ive pow'r That in our hearts, from this good

gin, Thy tem-ple deign to make us; Sun of the
hour, As fire it may be glow-ing; That we con-

soul, Thou Light Di-vine, A-round and in us bright-ly shine, To joy and
fess the Fa-ther, Son, And Thee, the Spir-it, Three in One, Thy glo-ry

glad-ness wake us That we, In Thee Tru-ly liv-ing, To Thee
ev-er show-ing. Stay Thou, Guide now Our souls ev-er That they

giv-ing Prayer un-ceas-ing, May in love be still in-creas-ing.
nev-er May for-sake Thee, But by faith their Ref-uge make Thee.

Text: Michael Schirmer (1606—73), cento; trans. Catherine Winkworth (1827—78), alt.
Tune: **Wie schön leuchtet**, *Philipp Nicolai (1556—1608)*

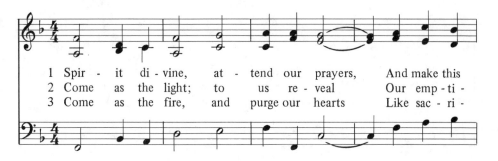

1 Spir - it di - vine, at - tend our prayers, And make this
2 Come as the light; to us re - veal Our emp - ti -
3 Come as the fire, and purge our hearts Like sac - ri -

house Thy home; De - scend with all Thy
ness and woe, And lead us in those
fi - cial flame; Let our whole soul an

gra - cious pow'rs, Oh, come, great Spir - it, come!
paths of life Where - on the righ - teous go.
of - f'ring be To our Re - deem - er's name.

4 Come as the Dove, and spread Thy wings,
The wings of peaceful love;
And let thy church on earth become
Blest as the church above.

5 Spirit divine, attend our prayers;
Make a lost world Thy home;
Descend with all Thy gracious powers;
Oh, come, great Spirit, come!

Text: Andrew Reed (1788—1862), cento
*Tune: **Nun danket all**, Johann Crueger (1598—1662)*

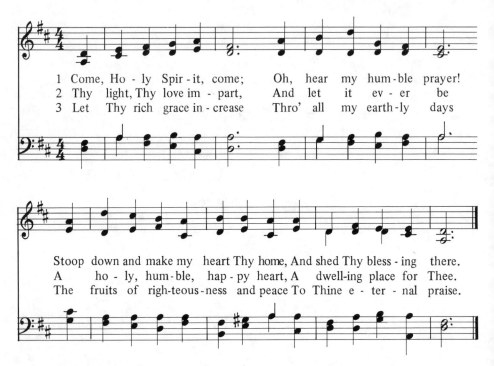

1 Come, Ho - ly Spir - it, come;   Oh, hear   my hum - ble prayer!
2 Thy light, Thy love im - part,   And let   it   ev - er   be
3 Let   Thy rich grace in - crease Thro' all   my earth - ly days

Stoop down and make my heart Thy home, And shed Thy bless - ing there.
A   ho - ly, hum - ble, hap - py heart, A   dwell-ing place for Thee.
The   fruits of righ-teous - ness and peace To Thine e - ter - nal praise.

Text: Dorothy A. Thrupp (1779—1847)
*Tune: **Franconia** (*Harmonischer Liederschatz, *Frankfurt, 1738)*

Pentecost was a great deal more than wind and fire,
    or even the utterance of strange languages
    by uneducated tongues.
The ascension or disappearance of Jesus did not signify
    God's departure from this world.
It was to prepare the way for His entrance into
    and His indwelling within
    the hearts of every one of His children.

                             (I Corinthians 12)

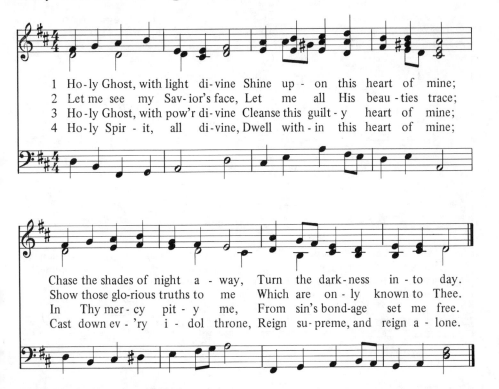

1 Ho-ly Ghost, with light di-vine Shine up - on this heart of mine;
2 Let me see my Sav-ior's face, Let me all His beau-ties trace;
3 Ho-ly Ghost, with pow'r di-vine Cleanse this guilt-y heart of mine;
4 Ho-ly Spir-it, all di-vine, Dwell with-in this heart of mine;

Chase the shades of night a - way, Turn the dark-ness in-to day.
Show those glo-rious truths to me Which are on-ly known to Thee.
In Thy mer-cy pit-y me, From sin's bond-age set me free.
Cast down ev-'ry i-dol throne, Reign su-preme, and reign a-lone.

Text: Andrew Reed (1788—1862), cento
*Tune: **Light Divine**, Orlando Gibbons (1583—1625)*

My heart is full of joy and contentment.
My mouth is filled with praises for You.
Even the night hours are no longer lonely
    as I contemplate Your tender concern for me.

The enemies of my soul still seek to betray me,
    but they shall not snatch me out of Your hand.
And now that I have found You,
    I shall be secure and happy forever.

                 (Psalm 63)

Holy God, We Praise Your Name

1 Ho - ly God, we praise Your name; Lord of all, we
2 Hark! the glad ce - les - tial hymn An - gel choirs a -
3 Lo, th' a - pos - tles' ho - ly train Join your sa - cred
4 Ho - ly Fa - ther, Ho - ly Son, Ho - ly Spir - it,

bow be - fore You. All on earth Your scep - ter claim,
bove are rais - ing; Cher - u - bim and ser - a - phim,
name to hal - low; Proph - ets swell the glad re - frain,
Three we name You Though in es - sence on - ly One;

All in heav'n a - bove a - dore You. In - fi - nite Your
In un - ceas - ing cho - rus prais - ing, Fill the heav'ns with
And the white-robed mar - tyrs fol - low, And from morn to
Un - di - vid - ed God we claim You And, a - dor - ing,

vast do - main, Ev - er - last - ing is Your reign.
sweet ac - cord: Ho - ly, ho - ly, ho - ly, Lord!
set of sun Thro' the church the song goes on.
bend the knee While we own the mys - ter - y. A - men.

Text: Anonymous 18th-century German Te Deum; trans. Clarence A. Walworth (1820—1900), alt.
*Tune: **Grosser Gott** (Allgemeines Katholisches Gesangbuch, Vienna, 1774)*

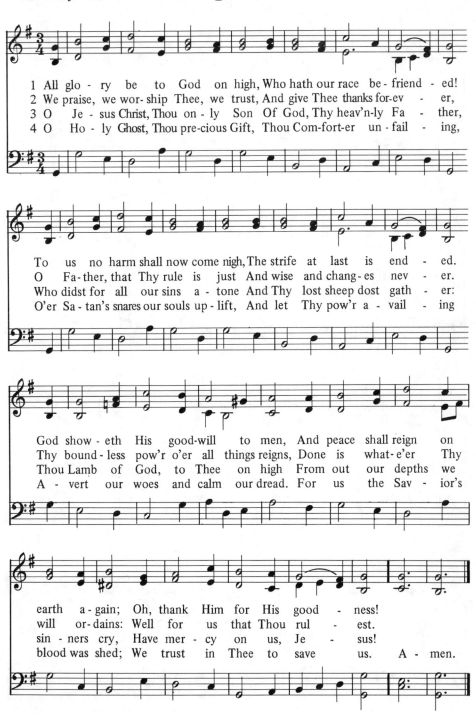

1 All glo-ry be to God on high, Who hath our race be-friend-ed!
2 We praise, we wor-ship Thee, we trust, And give Thee thanks for-ev - er,
3 O Je - sus Christ, Thou on - ly Son Of God, Thy heav'n-ly Fa - ther,
4 O Ho - ly Ghost, Thou pre-cious Gift, Thou Com-fort-er un - fail - ing,

To us no harm shall now come nigh, The strife at last is end - ed.
O Fa-ther, that Thy rule is just And wise and chang-es nev - er.
Who didst for all our sins a - tone And Thy lost sheep dost gath - er:
O'er Sa-tan's snares our souls up-lift, And let Thy pow'r a - vail - ing

God show-eth His good-will to men, And peace shall reign on
Thy bound-less pow'r o'er all things reigns, Done is what-e'er Thy
Thou Lamb of God, to Thee on high From out our depths we
A - vert our woes and calm our dread. For us the Sav - ior's

earth a-gain; Oh, thank Him for His good - ness!
will or-dains: Well for us that Thou rul - est.
sin - ners cry, Have mer - cy on us, Je - sus!
blood was shed; We trust in Thee to save us. A - men.

Text: Nikolaus Decius (c. 1485—c. 1546); trans. Catherine Winkworth (1827—78), alt.
Tune: Allein Gott in der Höh', Nikolaus Decius (c. 1485—c. 1546)

Holy, Holy, Holy! Lord God Almighty

1 Ho - ly, ho - ly, ho - ly! Lord God Al - might - y!
2 Ho - ly, ho - ly, ho - ly! Tho' the dark-ness hide Thee,
3 Ho - ly, ho - ly, ho - ly! Lord God Al - might - y!

Ear - ly in the morn - ing our song shall rise to Thee;
Tho' the eye of sin - ful man Thy glo - ry may not see,
All Thy works shall praise Thy name in earth and sky and sea.

Ho - ly, ho - ly, ho - ly, mer - ci - ful and might - y!
On - ly Thou art ho - ly, there is none be - side Thee,
Ho - ly, ho - ly, ho - ly, mer - ci - ful and might - y!

God in Three Per - sons, bless - ed Trin - i - ty!
Per - fect in pow'r, in love, and pu - ri - ty.
God in Three Per - sons, bless - ed Trin - i - ty! A - men.

Text: *Reginald Heber (1783—1826), cento*
Tune: *Nicaea, John B. Dykes (1823—76)*

I feel like singing this morning, O Lord.
I feel like telling everyone about me
      how great You are.
If only they could know the depths of Your love
      and Your eternal concern for those
         who will follow You!
But my songs are so often off-key.
My speech is so inadequate.
I simply cannot express what I feel,
      what I know to be true about Your love
         for Your creatures upon this world.

But even the songs of the birds
      proclaim Your praises.
The heavens and the earth beneath them,
        the trees that reach toward You,
        the flowers that glow in colorful beauty,
        the green hills and soaring mountains,
        the valleys and the plains,
        the lakes and the rivers,
        the great oceans that pound our shores —
      they proclaim Your greatness, O God,
        and Your love for the sons of men.

How glorious it is to be alive, O Lord!
May every breath of my body,
      every beat of my heart,
        be dedicated to Your praise and glory.
                (Psalm 89)

Faith
and the
Christian Life

71   Almighty God, Your Word Is Cast

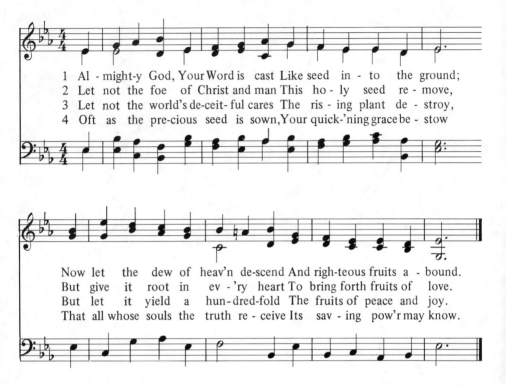

1 Al - might-y God, Your Word is cast Like seed in - to the ground;
2 Let not the foe of Christ and man This ho - ly seed re - move,
3 Let not the world's de-ceit- ful cares The ris - ing plant de - stroy,
4 Oft as the pre-cious seed is sown, Your quick-'ning grace be - stow

Now let the dew of heav'n de-scend And righ-teous fruits a - bound.
But give it root in ev - 'ry heart To bring forth fruits of love.
But let it yield a hun-dred-fold The fruits of peace and joy.
That all whose souls the truth re - ceive Its sav - ing pow'r may know.

Text: John Cawood (1775—1852), alt.
Tune: Dundee (Scottish Psalter, 1615)

There is something else we must learn as God's children.
It is not enough to be listeners and proclaimers
    of the Gospel;
      we are commissioned to be doers.
Christian faith that falls short of loving performance
    in respect to the needs of suffering people about us
    falls far short of genuine faith.
May our small faith be rekindled and burn bright
    with joy and obedience.
                      (James 1)

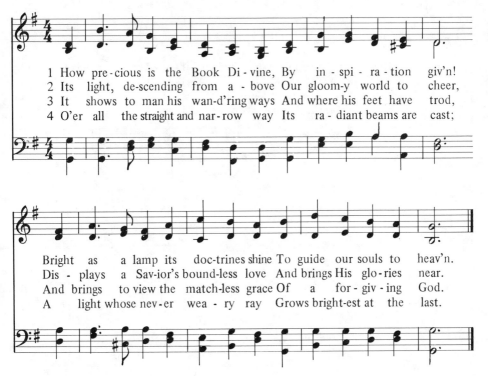

1 How pre-cious is the Book Di-vine, By in-spi-ra-tion giv'n!
2 Its light, de-scending from a-bove Our gloom-y world to cheer,
3 It shows to man his wan-d'ring ways And where his feet have trod,
4 O'er all the straight and nar-row way Its ra-diant beams are cast;

Bright as a lamp its doc-trines shine To guide our souls to heav'n.
Dis-plays a Sav-ior's bound-less love And brings His glo-ries near.
And brings to view the match-less grace Of a for-giv-ing God.
A light whose nev-er wea-ry ray Grows bright-est at the last.

Text: John Fawcett (1749—1817)
Tune: **Walder,** Johann Jakob Walder (1750—1817)

The way of salvation has been made possible through faith
 in what Christ has done for us and has been made
 plain in His Word to us.
We know of only one way to God.
It is the way of faith in God as revealed
 through His Son, our Lord.
This is the life that we are committed to live and the
 Gospel we are commanded to preach.
For us there is none other—nor need be.
Our God has found us, and we have returned to Him.

(II Peter 2)

1 The true Light that en-light-ens man, Al - le - lu - ia! Came to
2 And to all who be-lieve in Him, Al - le - lu - ia! Free-dom
3 Word made flesh has dwelt with man, Al - le - lu - ia! We shall
4 For the Law through Mo - ses came, Al - le - lu - ia! Grace and

earth from God's right hand, Al - le - lu - ia!
gave from bonds of sin, Al - le - lu - ia!
live with Him a - gain, Al - le - lu - ia!
truth in Je - sus' name, Al - le - lu - ia!

Refrain

Glo - ry be to Thee, O Lord, Al - le - lu - ia!

Praise to Thee, O Son of God, Al - le - lu - ia!

Text: John Ylvisaker (1937—), alt.
Tune: **Michael, row** (American Negro melody)

1 The law of God is good and wise
   And sets His will be-fore our eyes,
   Shows us the way of right-eous-ness,
   And dooms to death when we trans-gress.

2 To those who help in Christ have found
   And would in works of love a-bound
   It shows what deeds are His de-light
   And should be done as good and right.

3 The Law is good, but since the fall
   Its ho-li-ness con-demns us all;
   It dooms us for our sins to die
   And has no pow'r to jus-ti-fy.

4 The Gos-pel shows the Fa-ther's grace,
   Who sent His Son to save our race,
   Pro-claims how Je-sus lived and died
   That man might thus be jus-ti-fied.

5 It brings the Savior's righteousness
   Our souls to robe in royal dress;
   From all our guilt it brings release
   And gives the troubled conscience peace.

6 It is the power of God to save
   From sin and Satan and the grave;
   It works the faith, which firmly clings
   To all the treasures which it brings.

7 To Jesus we for refuge flee,
   Who from the curse has set us free,
   And humbly worship at His throne,
   Saved by His grace through faith alone.

Text: Matthias Loy (1828—1915), cento
Tune: Herr Jesu Christ, dich (Cantionale Germanicum, Dresden, 1628)

1 I was made a Chris-tian When my name was giv'n,
2 I must, like a Chris-tian, Shun all ev-il ways,
3 All a Chris-tian's bless-ings I will claim for mine:

One of God's dear chil-dren And an heir of heav'n.
Keep my faith in Je-sus, Serve Him all my days.
Ho-ly work and wor-ship, Fel-low-ship di-vine.

In the name of Chris-tian I will glo-ry now,
Called to be a Chris-tian, I will praise the Lord,
Fa-ther, Son, and Spir-it, Give me grace that I

Ev-er-more re-mem-ber My bap-tis-mal vow.
Seek for His as-sist-ance, So to keep my word.
Now may live a Chris-tian And a Chris-tian die.

Text: *John Samuel Jones (1831—1911)*
Tune: **Adoro te devote** *(French proper melody)*
Setting: *Paul Bunjes (1914—   )*

This is a joy-ous, hap-py day; We cel - e - brate Your gift of
life. Christ is with us, joy sur-rounds us. Christ takes our sin and sets us
free; He fills our lives with end-less life. Christ is with us; Christ u -
nites us. Praise our Mak - er, praise the Spir - it, Praise Christ Je - sus.

Text: Roger L. Tappert (1941—)
*Tune: **Lasst uns erfreuen** (Geistliche Kirchengesäng, Cologne, 1623)*
Setting: Ralph Vaughan Williams (1872—1958), alt.

77 Let All Things Now Living

1 Let all things now liv-ing A song of thanks-giv-ing To God the Cre - a - tor tri-
2 His law He en - forc-es, The stars in their cours-es, The sun in his or-bit, o -

um-phant-ly raise, Who fash-ioned and made us, Pro - tect-ed and stayed us, Who
be-dient - ly shine. The hills and the mountains, The riv-ers and fountains, The

still guides us on to the end of our days. His ban-ners are o'er us, His
deeps of the o-cean pro-claim Him di-vine. We too should be voic-ing Our

light goes be-fore us, A pil-lar of fire shin-ing forth in the night, Till shadows have
love and re-joic-ing; With glad ad-o - ra-tion a song let us raise Till all things now

van-ished And darkness is ban-ished, As for-ward we trav-el from light in-to light.
liv-ing U-nite in thanks-giv-ing To God in the high-est ho-san-na and praise!

Text: Katherine K. Davis (1892—); previously attributed to John Cowley
Tune: Ashgrove (traditional Welsh melody)

1 Sing-ing for Je - sus, our Sav - ior and King,
Sing - ing for Je - sus, the Lord whom we love;
All ad - o - ra - tion we joy - ous - ly bring,
Long-ing to praise as they praise Him a - bove.

2 Sing-ing for Je - sus, our Shep-herd and Guide,
Sing - ing for glad-ness of heart that He gives;
Sing-ing for won - der and praise that He died,
Sing - ing for bless-ing and joy that He lives.

Text: Francis R. Havergal (1836—79), cento
*Tune: **Slane** (traditional Irish melody)*
Setting: David N. Johnson (1922--)

Hal-le-lu! Hal-le-lu! Hal-le-lu! Hal-le-lu-jah! Praise ye the Lord!

Hal-le-lu! Hal-le-lu! Hal-le-lu! Hal-le-lu-jah! Praise ye the Lord!

Praise ye the Lord! Hal-le-lu-jah! Praise ye the Lord! Hal-le-lu-jah!

Praise ye the Lord! Hal-le-lu-jah! Praise ye the Lord!

Text: Traditional
*Tune: **Hallelujah!***

Amazing Grace

1 A - maz - ing grace! How sweet the sound That
2 'Twas grace that taught my heart to fear, And
3 Thro' man - y dan - gers, toils, and snares I
4 The Lord has prom - ised good to me, His

saved a wretch like me! I once was lost, but
grace my fears re - lieved; How pre - cious did that
have al - read - y come; 'Tis grace has brought me
Word my hope se - cures; He will my Shield and

now am found, Was blind, but now I see.
grace ap - pear The hour I first be - lieved!
safe thus far, And grace will lead me home.
Por - tion be, As long as life en - dures.

5 Yes, when this flesh and heart shall fail
And mortal life shall cease,
I shall possess, within the vail,
A life of joy and peace.

6 The earth shall soon dissolve in snow,
The sun forbear to shine;
But God, who called me here below,
Will be forever mine.

Text: John Newton (1725—1807)
Tune: Amazing grace (traditional American melody)
Setting: Edwin O. Excell (1851—1921)

1 Beau - ti - ful Sav - ior, King of Cre - a - tion, Son of
2 Fair are the mead - ows, Fair are the wood-lands, Robed in
3 Fair is the sun - shine, Fair is the moon-light, Bright the
4 Beau - ti - ful Sav - ior, Lord of the na - tions, Son of

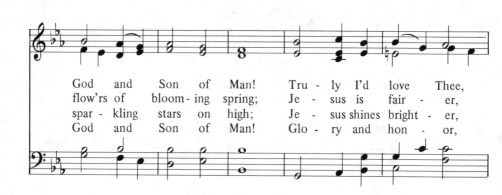

God and Son of Man! Tru - ly I'd love Thee,
flow'rs of bloom - ing spring; Je - sus is fair - er,
spar - kling stars on high; Je - sus shines bright - er,
God and Son of Man! Glo - ry and hon - or,

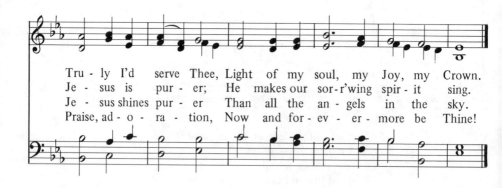

Tru - ly I'd serve Thee, Light of my soul, my Joy, my Crown.
Je - sus is pur - er; He makes our sor - r'wing spir - it sing.
Je - sus shines pur - er Than all the an - gels in the sky.
Praise, ad - o - ra - tion, Now and for - ev - er - more be Thine!

Text: *Anonymous* (Münster Gesangbuch, *1677), cento; trans. Joseph A. Seiss (1823—1904)*
Tune: ***Schönster Herr Jesu*** (Schlesische Volkslieder, *Leipzig, 1842)*
Setting: Martha F. Nye (1927—   )

1 For all the saints who from their la-bors rest,
  Who Thee by faith be-fore the world con-fessed,
  Thy name, O Je-sus, be for-ev-er blest.
  Al-le-lu-ia! Al-le-lu-ia!

2 Thou wast their Rock, their For-tress, and their Might;
  Thou, Lord, their Cap-tain in the well-fought fight;
  Thou, in the dark-ness drear, their one true Light.
  Al-le-lu-ia! Al-le-lu-ia!

3 Oh, may Thy sol-diers, faith-ful, true, and bold,
  Fight as the saints who no-bly fought of old
  And win with them the vic-tor's crown of gold.
  Al-le-lu-ia! Al-le-lu-ia!

4 O blest com-mu-nion, fel-low-ship di-vine,
  We fee-bly strug-gle, they in glo-ry shine;
  Yet all are one in Thee, for all are Thine.
  Al-le-lu-ia! Al-le-lu-ia!

A-men.

5 And when the fight is fierce, the warfare long,
  Steals on the ear the distant triumph song,
  And hearts are brave again, and arms are strong.
  Alleluia! Alleluia!

6 The golden evening brightens in the west;
  Soon, soon to faithful warriors cometh rest.
  Sweet is the calm of Paradise the blest.
  Alleluia! Alleluia!

7 But lo, there breaks a yet more glorious day;
  The saints triumphant rise in bright array;
  The King of Glory passes on His way.
  Alleluia! Alleluia!

8 From earth's wide bounds, from ocean's farthest coast,
  Through gates of pearl streams in the countless host,
  Singing to Father, Son, and Holy Ghost,
  Alleluia! Alleluia!

Text: William W. How (1823—97), cento
Tune: Sine nomine, Ralph Vaughan Williams (1872—1958)
Setting: Ralph Vaughan Williams (1872—1958), alt.

1 From all that dwell be-low the skies Let the Cre-a-tor's praise a-
2 E - ter-nal are Your mer-cies, Lord; E - ter-nal truth at-tends Your

rise; Al-le-lu-ia! Al-le-lu-ia! Let the Re-deem-er's name be
Word: Al-le-lu-ia! Al-le-lu-ia! Your praise shall sound from shore to

sung Thro' ev-'ry land, by ev-'ry tongue. Al-le-lu-ia! Al-le-
shore Till suns shall rise and set no more. Al-le-lu-ia! Al-le-

lu-ia! Al-le-lu-ia! Al-le-lu-ia! Al-le-lu-ia!
lu-ia! Al-le-lu-ia! Al-le-lu-ia! Al-le-lu-ia!

Text: Isaac Watts (1674—1748)
Tune: **Lasst uns erfreuen** (Geistliche Kirchengesäng, *Cologne, 1623)*
Setting: Ralph Vaughan Williams (1872—1958), alt.

1 Earth and all stars! Loud-rush-ing plan-ets,
2 Hail, wind, and rain! Loud-blow-ing snow-storm, Sing to the Lord
3 Trum-pet and pipes! Loud-clash-ing cym-bals,
4 En-gines and steel! Loud-pound-ing ham-mers,

_____ a new song!
O vic-to-ry! Loud-shout-ing ar-my,
Flow-ers and trees! Loud-rus-tling dry leaves,
Harp, lute, and lyre! Loud-hum-ming cel-los,
Lime-stone and beams! Loud-build-ing work-men,

Refrain
Sing to the Lord _____ a new song! He has done mar-

-vel-ous things. I too will praise Him with a new song!

5 Classrooms and labs!
Loud-boiling test tubes,
Sing to the Lord a new song!
Athlete and band!
Loud-cheering people,
Sing to the Lord a new song!
Refrain

6 Knowledge and truth!
Loud-sounding wisdom,
Sing to the Lord a new song!
Daughter and son!
Loud-praying members,
Sing to the Lord a new song!
Refrain

Text: Herbert Brokering (1926—)
*Tune: **Earth and all stars**, David N. Johnson (1922—)*
Setting: Jan Bender (1909—)

1 There is a name I love to hear; I love to sing its worth. It
2 It tells me of a Sav-ior's love, Who died to set me free. It
3 It tells me what my Fa-ther hath In store for ev-'ry day And,
4 It tells of One whose lov-ing heart Can feel my deep-est woe, Who

sounds like mu-sic in my ear, The sweet-est name on earth.
tells me of His pre-cious blood, The sin-ner's per-fect plea.
though I tread a dark-some path, Yields sun-shine all the way.
in each sor-row bears a part That none can bear be-low.

Refrain

Oh, how I love Je-sus! Oh, how I love Je-sus!

Oh, how I love Je-sus, be-cause He first loved me!

Text: Frederick Whitfield (1829—1904)
Tune: *Oh, how I love Jesus* (anonymous 19th-century American melody)

1 Praise to the Lord, the Al-might-y, the King of cre-a-
tion! O my soul, praise Him, for He is your Health and Sal-
va-tion! Let all who hear Now to His
tem-ple draw near, Join me in glad ad-o-ra-tion!

2 Praise to the Lord, who o'er all things is won-drous-ly reign-
ing And as on wings of an ea-gle, up-lift-ing, sus-
tain-ing. Have you not seen All that is
need-ful has been Grant-ed by gra-cious or-dain-ing?

3 Praise to the Lord, who has fear-ful-ly, won-drous-ly, made
you; Giv-en you health and, when heed-less-ly fall-ing, has
stayed you. What need or grief Ev-er has
failed of re-lief? Wings of His mer-cy did shade you.

4 Praise to the Lord, who will prosper your work and defend you;
Who from the heavens the streams of His mercy still sends you.
Ponder anew
What the Almighty can do
Since with His love He befriends you.

5 Praise to the Lord! Oh, let all that is in me adore Him!
All that has life and breath, come now with praises before Him!
Let the amen
Sound from His people again;
Gladly forever adore Him.

Text: Joachim Neander (1650—80); trans. Catherine Winkworth (1827—78), alt.
Tune: *Lobe den Herren, den* (Erneuertes Gesangbuch, Part II, *Stralsund, 1665*), adapted

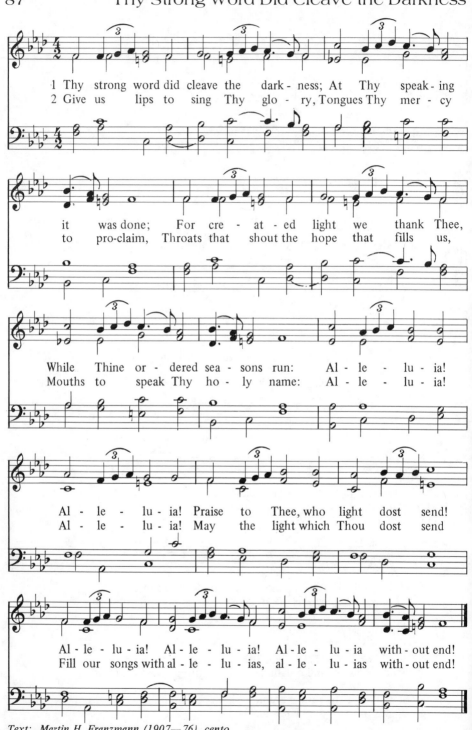

1 Thy strong word did cleave the dark-ness; At Thy speak-ing
2 Give us lips to sing Thy glo-ry, Tongues Thy mer-cy

it was done; For cre-at-ed light we thank Thee,
to pro-claim, Throats that shout the hope that fills us,

While Thine or-dered sea-sons run: Al - le - lu - ia!
Mouths to speak Thy ho-ly name: Al - le - lu - ia!

Al - le - lu - ia! Praise to Thee, who light dost send!
Al - le - lu - ia! May the light which Thou dost send

Al - le - lu - ia! Al - le - lu - ia! Al - le - lu - ia with-out end!
Fill our songs with al - le - lu - ias, al - le - lu - ias with-out end!

Text: *Martin H. Franzmann (1907—76), cento*
Tune: **Ebenezer**, *Thomas John Williams (1869–1944)*
Setting: *Richard Hillert (1923—)*

1 All hail the pow'r of Je - sus' name! Let an - gels pros - trate fall;
2 You seed of Is - rael's cho - sen race, You ran-somed from the fall,
3 Let ev - 'ry kin - dred, ev - 'ry tribe On this ter - res - trial ball
4 Oh, that with yon - der sa - cred throng We at His feet may fall!

Bring forth the roy - al di - a - dem, And crown Him Lord of all.
Hail Him who saves you by His grace, And crown Him Lord of all.
To   Him all maj - es - ty as - cribe, And crown Him Lord of all.
We'll join the ev - er - last - ing song And crown Him Lord of all.

Bring forth the roy - al di - a - dem, And crown Him Lord of all.
Hail Him who saves you by His grace, And crown Him Lord of all.
To   Him all maj - es - ty as - cribe, And crown Him Lord of all.
We'll join the ev - er - last - ing song And crown Him Lord of all.

Text: Edward Perronet (1716—92), cento, alt.
Tune: **Coronation**, Oliver Holden (1765—1844)

1 For the beau-ty of the earth, For the glo-ry of the skies,
2 For the won-der of each hour Of the day and of the night,
3 For the joy of hu-man love, Broth-er, sis-ter, par-ent, child,
4 For Thy church that ev-er-more Lift-eth ho-ly hands a-bove,

For the love which from our birth O-ver and a-round us lies,
Hill and vale, and tree and flow'r, Sun and moon, and stars of light,
Friends on earth and friends a-bove, For all gen-tle thoughts and mild,
Off-'ring up on ev-'ry shore Her pure sac-ri-fice of love,

Christ, our God, to Thee we raise This our hymn of grate-ful praise.

Text: Folliott Sanford Pierpoint (1835—1907)
*Tune: **Dix**, Conrad Kocher (1786—1872); adapted by William H. Monk (1823—89)*

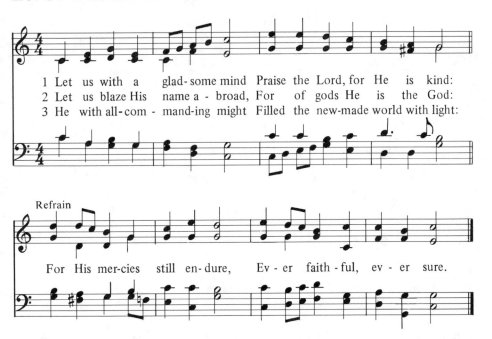

1 Let us with a glad-some mind Praise the Lord, for He is kind:
2 Let us blaze His name a - broad, For of gods He is the God:
3 He with all-com - mand-ing might Filled the new-made world with light:

Refrain

For His mer-cies still en-dure, Ev - er faith - ful, ev - er sure.

4 All things living He doth feed;
His full hand supplies their need:
Refrain

5 Let us then with gladsome mind
Praise the Lord, for He is kind:
Refrain

Text: John Milton (1608—74), cento
Tune: Monkland, John Antes (1740—1811)
Setting: John Bernard Wilkes (1785—1869), alt.

Where should I look for help in my need?
To majestic mountain peaks that probe our skies
　　　or to giants of industry that hem in our cities?
To satellites that circle our world
　　　or to computers that store up our knowledge?

The answer to my problems
　　　and the fulfillment of my needs
　　　must come from God Himself,
　　　from Him who created skies and mountains
　　　and man to dwell in their midst.

(Psalm 121)

1 This is my Fa-ther's world, And to my lis-t'ning ears All
2 This is my Fa-ther's world; The birds their car-ols raise; The
3 This is my Fa-ther's world; Oh, let me ne'er for-get That

na-ture sings, and round me rings The mu-sic of the spheres.
morn-ing light, the lil-y white, De-clare their Mak-er's praise.
though the wrong seems oft so strong, God is the Rul-er yet.

This is my Fa-ther's world; I rest me in the thought Of
This is my Fa-ther's world; He shines in all that's fair; In the
This is my Fa-ther's world; Why should my heart be sad? The

rocks and trees, of skies and seas, His hand the won-ders wrought.
rus-tling grass I hear Him pass, He speaks to me ev-'ry-where.
Lord is King, let the heav-ens ring; God reigns, let the earth be glad!

Text: Maltbie Davenport Babcock (1858—1901)
Tune: **Terra patris,** *Franklin Lawrence Sheppard (1852—1930)*

My lips shall praise Thee: Thus shall I bless Thee.

I will lift up my hands un-to the Lord.

Text: Traditional
Tune: Loving-kindness
Setting: Charles Ore (1936—)

And God Said, Yes!

1 And God said, Yes! Yes! Yes! / Said yes to the world once more, / Said yes with a cos-mic roar, / Said o-pen that oth-er door, / Said yes, yes, yes, man, yes!

Yes! Yes! Yes! / Let's splash the sky with light, / Let's float the earth in space, / Let's dance a-way the night, / Said yes, yes, yes, man, yes!

Yes! Yes! Yes! / Let's make a man who's free, / Cre-at-ing life with love / And rul-ing earth with Me, / Said yes, yes, yes, man, yes!

Yes! Yes! Yes! / Let Je-sus Christ be born! / Let's find Him in the straw! / Let's blast the shep-herd's horn! / Said yes, yes, yes, Son, yes!

5 And God said, Yes! Yes! Yes!
Yes to His broken Son!
Yes to His open wound!
Yes to the broken tomb!
Said yes, yes, yes, Son, yes!

6 And God said Yes! Yes! Yes!
We'll leap the swirling sky!
We'll leap the hungry grave!
We'll never stop to die!
Said yes, yes, yes, man, yes!

7 And God said, Yes! Yes! Yes!
Says yes to that other door!
Says yes when men say no!
Says yes with a cosmic roar!
Says yes, yes, yes, with me!

Text: Norman C. Habel (1932—)
*Tune: **Yes**, Richard Koehneke (1945—)*
Setting: Charles Ore (1936—)

1 Come praise the Lord, You chil-dren of the Lord.
2 Come bless His name, You chil-dren of the Lord.
3 Re - joice in God; His love de - scends on us.

Come raise your voice In joy - ous song.
Come sing His praise, And let the trum - pet sound.
Lift up your voice, And sound His name a - far.

Refrain
Al - le - lu - ia, al - le - lu - ia,

al - le - lu - ia, al - le - lu - ia!

Text: Gregory Miller (1937—)
Tune: **Come praise the Lord,** *Gregory Miller (1937—)*

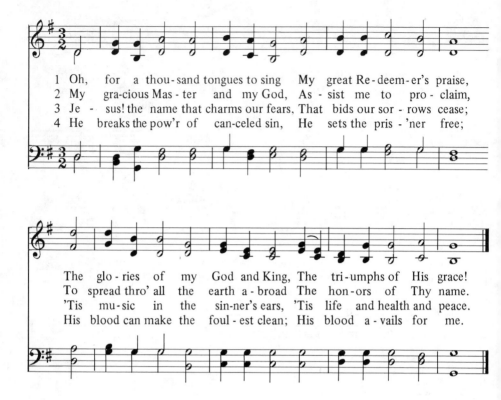

1 Oh, for a thou-sand tongues to sing My great Re-deem-er's praise,
2 My gra-cious Mas-ter and my God, As-sist me to pro-claim,
3 Je-sus! the name that charms our fears, That bids our sor-rows cease;
4 He breaks the pow'r of can-celed sin, He sets the pris-'ner free;

The glo-ries of my God and King, The tri-umphs of His grace!
To spread thro' all the earth a-broad The hon-ors of Thy name.
'Tis mu-sic in the sin-ner's ears, 'Tis life and health and peace.
His blood can make the foul-est clean; His blood a-vails for me.

5 Look unto Him, ye nations; own
Your God, ye fallen race.
Look and be saved through faith alone,
Be justified by grace.

6 See all your sins on Jesus laid;
The Lamb of God was slain;
His soul was once an offering made
For every soul of man.

7 Glory to God and praise and love
Be ever, ever given
By saints below and saints above,
The church in earth and heaven.

Text: Charles Wesley (1707—88), cento
Tune: Azmon, Carl G. Glazer (1784—1829)
Setting: Lowell Mason (1792—1872)

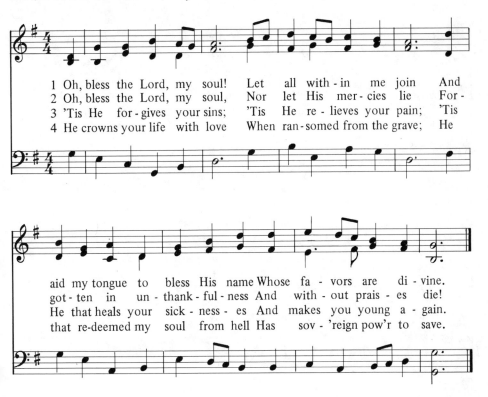

1 Oh, bless the Lord, my soul! Let all with-in me join And aid my tongue to bless His name Whose fa-vors are di-vine.

2 Oh, bless the Lord, my soul, Nor let His mer-cies lie For-got-ten in un-thank-ful-ness And with-out prais-es die!

3 'Tis He for-gives your sins; 'Tis He re-lieves your pain; 'Tis He that heals your sick-ness-es And makes you young a-gain.

4 He crowns your life with love When ran-somed from the grave; He that re-deemed my soul from hell Has sov-'reign pow'r to save.

5 He fills the poor with good;
He gives the sufferers rest:
The Lord has judgments for the proud
And justice for th' opprest.

6 His wondrous works and ways
He made by Moses known,
But sent the world His truth and grace
By His beloved Son.

Text: Isaac Watts (1674—1748)
Tune: St. Thomas, Aaron Williams (1731—76)

You Servants of God

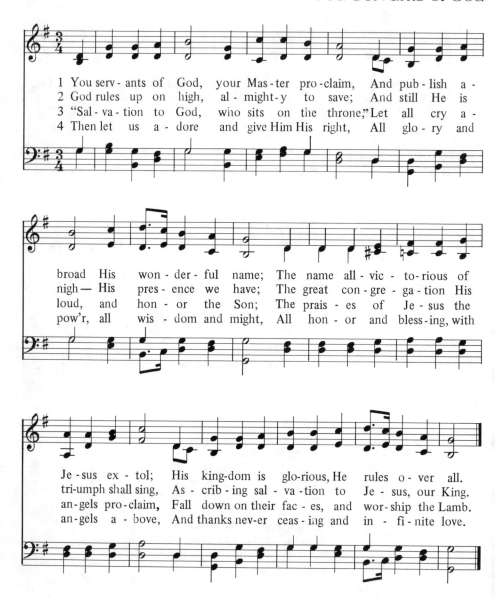

1 You serv-ants of God, your Mas-ter pro-claim, And pub-lish a-
2 God rules up on high, al-might-y to save; And still He is
3 "Sal-va-tion to God, who sits on the throne,"Let all cry a-
4 Then let us a-dore and give Him His right, All glo-ry and

broad His won-der-ful name; The name all-vic-to-rious of
nigh— His pres-ence we have; The great con-gre-ga-tion His
loud, and hon-or the Son; The prais-es of Je-sus the
pow'r, all wis-dom and might, All hon-or and bless-ing, with

Je-sus ex-tol; His king-dom is glo-rious, He rules o-ver all.
tri-umph shall sing, As-crib-ing sal-va-tion to Je-sus, our King.
an-gels pro-claim, Fall down on their fac-es, and wor-ship the Lamb.
an-gels a-bove, And thanks nev-er ceas-ing and in-fi-nite love.

Text: Charles Wesley (1707—88), cento, alt.
Tune: Lyons, J. Michael Haydn (1737—1806); arr. William Gardiner (1770—1853)

1 Oh, that I had a thou-sand voic - es To praise my God with thou-sand tongues! My heart, which in the Lord re - joic - es, Would then pro-claim in grate-ful songs To all, wher-ev - er I might be, What great things God has done for me.

2 O all you pow'rs that He im-plant - ed, A - rise, keep si - lence now no more; Put forth the strength that God has grant - ed! Your no blest work is to a - dore! O soul and bod - y, join to raise With heart-felt joy our Mak - er's praise.

3 You for-est leaves so green and ten - der That dance for joy in sum - mer air, You mead-ow grass - es, bright and slen - der, You flow'rs so fra-grant and so fair, You live to show God's praise a - lone. Join me to make His glo - ry known.

4 All creatures that have breath and motion,
That throng the earth, the sea, the sky,
Come, share with me my heart's devotion,
Help me to sing God's praises high!
My utmost powers can never quite
Declare the wonders of His might!

5 Creator, humbly I implore you
To listen to my earthly song,
Until that day when I adore you,
When I have joined the angel throng
And learned with choirs of heaven
  to sing
Eternal anthems to my King!

Text: Johann Mentzer (1658—1734), cento; trans. composite
*Tune: **O dass ich tausend**, Johann B. König (1691—1758)*

Thanks be to God, the Fa-ther Al - might - y! Thanks be to God, who came to this earth! Thanks be to God, the Spir-it E - ter - nal! Thanks be to God for - ev - er!

Text: John Ylvisaker (1937—)
*Tune: **Thanks be to God,** John Ylvisaker (1937—)*
Setting: John Ylvisaker (1937—)

100   God, Who Stretched the Spangled Heavens

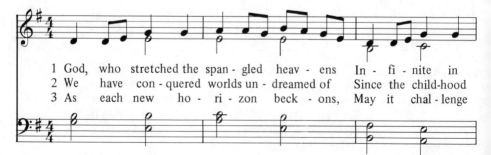

1 God, who stretched the span - gled heav - ens In - fi - nite in
2 We have con - quered worlds un - dreamed of Since the child-hood
3 As each new ho - ri - zon beck - ons, May it chal - lenge

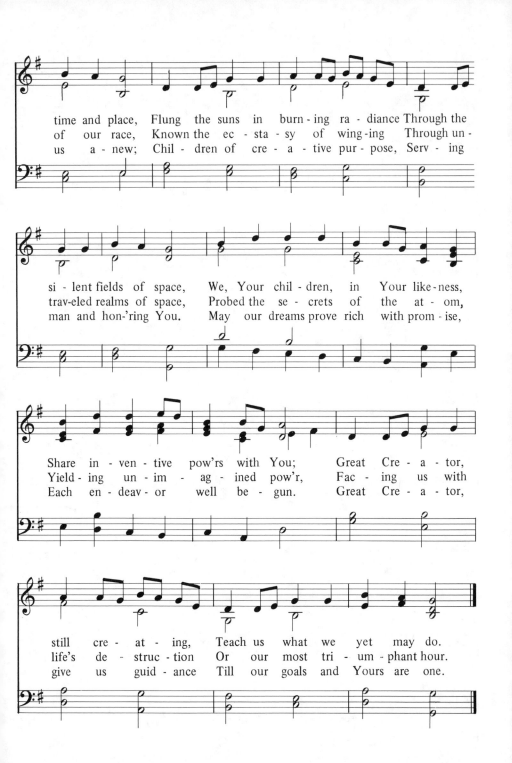

time and place, Flung the suns in burn-ing ra-diance Through the
of our race, Known the ec-sta-sy of wing-ing Through un-
us a-new; Chil-dren of cre-a-tive pur-pose, Serv-ing

si-lent fields of space, We, Your chil-dren, in Your like-ness,
trav-eled realms of space, Probed the se-crets of the at-om,
man and hon-'ring You. May our dreams prove rich with prom-ise,

Share in-ven-tive pow'rs with You; Great Cre-a-tor,
Yield-ing un-im-ag-ined pow'r, Fac-ing us with
Each en-deav-or well be-gun. Great Cre-a-tor,

still cre-at-ing, Teach us what we yet may do.
life's de-struc-tion Or our most tri-um-phant hour.
give us guid-ance Till our goals and Yours are one.

Text: Catherine C. (Arnott) Cameron (1927—   ); rev. by author
Tune: **Holy manna** (Southern Harmony, *1835)*
Setting: Charles R. Anders (1929—   )

1 In Thee is glad - ness A - mid all sad - ness, Je - sus,
2 If He is ours, We fear no pow - ers, Not of

Sun - shine of my heart. By Thee are giv - en The gifts of
earth nor sin nor death. He sees and bless - es In worst dis-

heav - en, Thou the true Re-deem - er art. Our souls Thou
tress - es, He can change them with a breath. Where-fore the

wak - est, Our bonds Thou break - est; Who trusts Thee sure - ly Has built se-
sto - ry Tell of His glo - ry With hearts and voic - es, All heav'n re-

cure - ly, He stands for - ev - er. Al - le - lu - ia! Our hearts are
joic - es In Him for - ev - er. Al - le - lu - ia! We shout for

pin - ing To see Thy shin - ing, Dy-ing or liv - ing To Thee are
glad - ness, Tri-umph o'er sad - ness,Love Him and praise Him And still shall

cleav - ing, Naught can us sev - er. Al - le - lu - ia!
raise Him Glad hymns for - ev - er. Al - le - lu - ia!

Text: Johann Lindemann (1549—c.1631); trans. Catherine Winkworth (1829—78)
Tune: **In dir ist Freude**, Giovanni Giacomo Gastoldi (c.1556--1622)
Setting: Jan Bender (1909—)

Praise God, from Whom All Blessings Flow   102

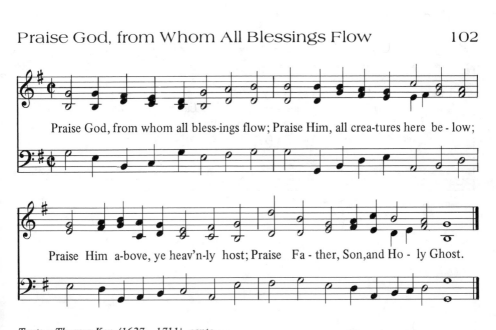

Praise God, from whom all bless-ings flow; Praise Him, all crea-tures here be - low;

Praise Him a-bove, ye heav'n-ly host; Praise Fa - ther, Son,and Ho - ly Ghost.

Text: Thomas Ken (1637—1711), cento
Tune: **Old Hundredth**, Louis Bourgeois (c.1510—61)

1 Glo - ry be to God the Fa - ther, Glo - ry be to
2 Glo - ry be to Him who loved us, Washed us from each
3 Glo - ry to the King of an - gels, Glo - ry to the
4 Glo - ry, bless - ing, praise e - ter - nal! Thus the choir of

God the Son, Glo - ry be to God the Spir - it: Great Je - ho - vah,
spot and stain; Glo - ry be to Him who bo't us, Made us kings with
church's King, Glo - ry to the King of na - tions; Heav'n and earth, your
an - gels sings; Hon - or, rich - es, pow'r, do - min - ion! Thus its praise cre -

Three in One! Glo - ry, glo - ry While e - ter - nal a - ges run!
Him to reign! Glo - ry, glo - ry To the Lamb that once was slain!
prais - es bring! Glo - ry, glo - ry To the King of Glo - ry sing!
a - tion brings. Glo - ry, glo - ry, Glo - ry to the King of kings!

Text: *Horatius Bonar (1808—99)*
Tune: **Worcester**, *Walter G. Whinfield (1865—1919)*

1 We praise You, O God, our Re - deem - er, Cre - a - tor, In grate - ful de -
2 We wor - ship You, God of our fa - thers, we bless You; Thro' tri - al and
3 With voic - es u - nit - ed our prais - es we of - fer And glad - ly our

vo - tion our trib - ute we bring; We lay it be - fore You, we
tem - pest our guide You have been. When per - ils o'er - take us, Your
songs of thanks-giv - ing we raise. With You, Lord, be - side us, Your

kneel and a - dore You, We bless Your ho - ly name, glad prais - es we sing.
love will not for - sake us, And with Your help, O Lord, our strug - gles we win.
strong arm will guide us. To You, our great Re - deem - er, for - ev - er be praise!

Text: Julia B. Cady Cory (1882—1963), alt.
*Tune: **Kremser** (traditional Dutch tune; Nederlandtsch Gedenckclanck, Haarlem, 1626)*

Text: Martin Rinkart (1586—1649); trans. Catherine Winkworth (1827—78)
Tune: **Nun danket alle Gott**, Johann Crueger (1598—1662)

1 Come, ye thank-ful peo-ple, come; Raise the song of har-vest home.
2 All the world is God's own field, Fruit un-to His praise to yield;
3 For the Lord, our God, shall come And shall take His har-vest home;
4 E-ven so, Lord, quick-ly come To Thy fi-nal har-vest home;

All be safe-ly gath-ered in Ere the win-ter storms be-gin;
Wheat and tares to-geth-er sown, Un-to joy or sor-row grown;
From His field shall in that day All of-fens-es purge a-way;
Gath-er Thou Thy peo-ple in, Free from sor-row, free from sin,

God, our Mak-er, doth pro-vide For our wants to be sup-plied.
First the blade and then the ear, Then the full corn shall ap-pear.
Give His an-gels charge at last In the fire the tares to cast
There, for-ev-er pu-ri-fied, In Thy gar-ner to a-bide.

Come to God's own tem-ple, come; Raise the song of har-vest home.
Lord of har-vest, grant that we Whole-some grain and pure may be.
But the fruit-ful ears to store In His gar-ner ev-er-more.
Come with all Thine an-gels, come, Raise the glo-rious har-vest home.

Text: Henry Alford (1810—71), cento, alt.
*Tune: **St. George**, George J. Elvey (1816—93)*

1 God bless our na-tive land! Firm may she ev-er stand Thro' storm and night!
2 For her our prayer shall rise To God a-bove the skies; On Him we wait.

When the wild tem-pests rave, Rul-er of wind and wave,
Thou who art ev-er nigh, Guard-ing with watch-ful eye,

Do Thou our coun-try save By Thy great might.
To Thee a-loud we cry, God save the State!

Text: *Siegfried A. Mahlmann (1771—1826); trans. Charles Timothy Brooks (1813—83)*
         and John Sullivan Dwight (1813—93)
Tune: **America** (Thesaurus Musicus, *England, 1740)*

1 Sing to the Lord of har - vest, Sing songs of love and
2 By Him the clouds drop fat - ness, The des - erts bloom and
3 Bring to His sa - cred al - tar The gifts His good-ness

praise; With joy - ful hearts and voic - es Your all - le - lu - ias
spring, The hills leap up in glad - ness, The val - leys laugh and
gave, The gold - en sheaves of har - vest, The souls He died to

raise. By Him the roll - ing sea - sons In fruit - ful or - der
sing. He fill - eth with His full - ness All things with large in -
save. Your hearts lay down be - fore Him When at His feet you

move; Sing to the Lord of har - vest A joy-ous song of love.
crease, He crowns the year with good - ness, With plen-ty and with peace.
fall, And with your lives a - dore Him, Who gave His life for all.

Text: John S.B. Monsell (1811—75)
*Tune: **Wie lieblich ist der Maien**, Johann Steurlein (1546—1613)*
Setting: S. Drummond Wolff (1916—)

109 Wake Us, O Lord, to Human Need

1 Wake us, O Lord, to human need To
2 Un - blind our eyes so we may see The
3 Lord, free our hands for heal - ing touch To
4 Since you've re - deemed us from de - spair, You've

go wher - ev - er You would lead. A - wake our sens - es
masks that cov - er mis - er - y, The hid - den tear, the
reach to those who've suf - fered much: Re - tard - ed child, de -
freed us so that we can share; Our neigh - bors' prob - lems

so that we More sen - si - tive to needs may be.
wor - ried frown, The lone - li - ness of those let down.
lin - quent, poor; Your love, a - live in us, the cure.
now we'll bear. Be - cause You love, we love and care!

Text: Phyllis Kersten (1939—)
Tune: **Tallis' Canon**, Thomas Tallis (c.1510—85)

1 O God of mer - cy, God of might, In love and
2 And Thou, who cam'st on earth to die That fall - en
3 Teach us the les - son Thou hast taught, To feel for
4 All are re - deemed, both far and wide, Since Thou, O

pit - y in - fin - ite, Teach us, as ev - er
men might live there - by, Oh, hear us; for to
those Thy blood hath bought, That ev - 'ry word and
Lord, for all hast died. Oh, teach us what - so -

in Thy sight, To live our life to Thee.
Thee we cry, In hope, O Lord, to Thee.
deed and thought May work a work for Thee.
e'er be - tide, To love them all in Thee!

Text: Godfrey Thring (1823—1903), cento
*Tune: **Dunstan**, Joseph Barnby (1838—86)*

1 We thank You, Lord, for eyes to see The beau-ty of the earth;
2 Help us re-mem-ber that to some The eye and ear and mind
3 Oh, may our eyes be o-pen, Lord, To see our neigh-bors' need;

For ears to hear the words of love And hap-py sounds of mirth;
Bring sights and sounds of ug-li-ness And on-ly sad-ness find;
And may our ears be kept a-lert Their cries for help to heed;

For minds that find new thoughts to think, New won-ders to ex-plore;
Help us re-mem-ber that to them The world has seemed un-fair,
Make keen our minds to plan the best For one an-oth-er's good,

For health and free-dom to en-joy The good You have in store.
That we must strive to give to them The beau-ty all may share.
That all the world may be at last One friend-ly neigh-bor-hood.

Text: *Jeanette E. Perkins (1887—1960)*
Tune: **Ellacombe** (Gesangbuch, *Württemberg, 1784)*

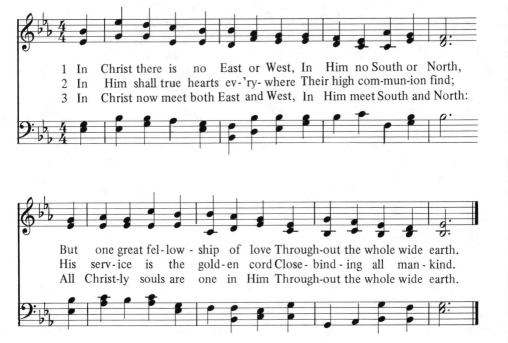

1 In Christ there is no East or West, In Him no South or North,
2 In Him shall true hearts ev-'ry-where Their high com-mun-ion find;
3 In Christ now meet both East and West, In Him meet South and North:

But one great fel-low-ship of love Through-out the whole wide earth.
His serv-ice is the gold-en cord Close-bind-ing all man-kind.
All Christ-ly souls are one in Him Through-out the whole wide earth.

Text: *John Oxenham (1852—1941), cento*
Tune: **St. Peter,** *Alexander R. Reinagle (1799—1877)*

It is God's love as manifested in Christ
    that makes us equal, in God's eyes, with all persons.
And it makes all persons equal with us.
We differ in many ways—
    in intellect, talents, training and temperament,
    background and opportunity.
Under God, however, there is no distinction.
His all-encompassing love levels all barriers
    and accounts every human creature
    of equal value and worth.
There are no strangers or aliens in God's family,
    only brothers and sisters,
And all of us are members of the one body,
    the body of Christ,
    and are commissioned to work together
    in carrying out His purposes.

(Ephesians 2)

1 God of grace and God of glo - ry, On Your peo - ple
2 Lo! the hosts of e - vil round us Scorn the Christ, as -
3 Cure Your chil - dren's war - ring mad-ness; Bend our pride to
4 Save us from weak res - ig-na - tion To the e - vils

pour Your pow'r; Crown Your an - cient church - 's sto - ry;
sail His ways! From the fears that long have bound us
Your con - trol; Shame our wan - ton, sel - fish glad - ness,
we de - plore; Let the gift of Your sal - va - tion

Bring her bud to glo-rious flow'r. Grant us wis - dom, Grant us cour-age
Free our hearts to faith and praise. Grant us wis - dom, Grant us cour-age
Rich in things and poor in soul. Grant us wis - dom, Grant us cour-age
Be our glo - ry ev - er - more. Grant us wis - dom, Grant us cour-age

For the fac-ing of this hour, For the fac - ing of this hour.
For the liv-ing of these days, For the liv - ing of these days.
Lest we miss Your king-dom's goal, Lest we miss Your king-dom's goal.
Serv - ing You, whom we a-dore, Serv-ing You, whom we a - dore.

Text: Harry Emerson Fosdick (1878—1969), cento, alt.
Tune: **Cwm Rhondda,** John Hughes (1873—1932)
Setting: Paul Bunjes (1914—)

1 Lord of all na - tions, grant me grace To love all
2 Break down the wall that would di - vide Thy chil - dren,
3 For - give me, Lord, where I have erred By love - less

peo - ple, ev - 'ry race And in each mor - tal may I
Lord, on ev - 'ry side. My neigh-bor's good let me pur -
act and thought-less word. Make me to see the wrong I

see My kin - dred, loved, re- deemed by Thee.
sue, Let Chris - tian love bind warm and true.
do Will cru - ci - fy my Lord a - new.

4 Give me Thy courage, Lord, to speak
Whenever strong oppress the weak.
Should I myself the victim be,
Help me forgive, remembering Thee.

5 With Thine own love may I be filled
And by Thy Holy Spirit willed,
That all I touch, where'er I be,
May be divinely touched by Thee.

Text: Olive Wise Spannaus (1916—), rev. by author
*Tune: **Beatus Vir** (Slovak melody, 1561)*
Setting: Richard Hillert (1923—)

115 I Love to Tell the Story

1. I love to tell the sto - ry Of un - seen things a - bove, Of
2. I love to tell the sto - ry, 'Tis pleas - ant to re - peat What
3. I love to tell the sto - ry, For those who know it best Seem

Je - sus and His glo - ry, Of Je - sus and His love. I love to tell the
seems, each time I tell it, More won - der - ful - ly sweet. I love to tell the
hun - ger - ing and thirst - ing To hear it like the rest. And when in scenes of

sto - ry, Be - cause I know it's true; It sat - is - fies my long - ings As
sto - ry, For some have nev - er heard The mes - sage of sal - va - tion From
glo - ry I sing the new, new song, 'Twill be the old, old sto - ry That

Refrain

noth - ing else would do.
God's own ho - ly Word. I love to tell the sto - ry; 'Twill be my theme in
I have loved so long.

glo - ry To tell the old, old sto - ry Of Je - sus and His love.

Text: *Arabella Katherine Hankey (1834--1911)*
Tune: **Hankey**, *William Gustavus Fischer (1835--1912)*

1 Bless-ed as - sur - ance, Je - sus is mine! Oh, what a fore-taste of
2 Per-fect sub-mis - sion, per-fect de - light, Vi-sions of rap - ture now
3 Per-fect sub-mis - sion, all is at rest, I in my Sav - ior am

glo - ry di - vine! Heir of sal - va - tion, pur-chase of God, Born of His
burst on my sight; An - gels de-scend-ing, bring from a - bove Ech-oes of
hap - py and blest, Watch-ing and wait-ing, look-ing a - bove Filled with His

Refrain

Spir - it, washed in His blood.
mer - cy, whis-pers of love. This is my sto - ry, this is my
good-ness, lost in His love.

song, Prais-ing my Sav - ior all the day long; This is my

sto - ry, this is my song, Prais-ing my Sav-ior all the day long.

Text: Fanny J. Crosby (1823—1915)
Tune: **Assurance,** Phoebe P. Knapp (1839—1908)

Refrain

What-so-ev-er you do to the least of My broth-ers, That you

do un-to Me.
1 When I was hun-gry, you gave Me to eat;____
2 When I was wea-ry, you helped Me find rest;____
3 Hurt in a bat-tle, you bound up My wounds;____
4 When I was Ne-gro or Chi-nese or white,____

When I was thirst-y, you gave Me to drink.____
When I was an-xious, you calmed all My fears.____
Search-ing for kind-ness, you held out your hand.____
Mocked and in-sult-ed, I car-ried My cross.____

Now en-ter in-to the home of My Fa - ther.____

5 When I was homeless, you opened your door;
When I was naked, you gave Me your coat.

6 When I was little, you taught Me to read;
When I was lonely, you gave Me your love.

7 When in a prison, you came to My cell;
When on a sick bed, you cared for My needs.

8 In a strange country, you made Me at home;
  Seeking employment, you found Me a job.

9 When I was aged, you bothered to smile;
  When I was restless, you listened and cared.

10 You saw Me covered with spittle and blood;
   You knew My features though grimy with sweat.

11 When I was laughed at, you stood by My side;
   When I was happy, you shared in My joy.

Text: *Willard F. Jabusch (1930—)*
Tune: ***Whatsoever you do,*** *Willard F. Jabusch (1930—)*
Setting: *Charles Ore (1936—)*

Spread, Oh, Spread, Thou Mighty Word   118

1 Spread, oh, spread, thou might-y Word, Spread the king-dom of the Lord,
2 Tell them how the Fa-ther's will Made the world and keeps it still,
3 Tell of our Re-deem-er's love, Who for-ev-er doth re-move
4 Tell them of the Spir-it giv'n Now to guide us up to heav'n,

Where-so-e'er His breath has giv'n Life to be-ings meant for heav'n.
How His on-ly Son He gave Man from sin and death to save.
By His ho-ly sac-ri-fice All the guilt that on us lies.
Strong and ho-ly, just and true, Work-ing both to will and do.

5 Up! The ripening fields ye see.
  Mighty shall the harvest be;
  But the reapers still are few,
  Great the work they have to do.

6 Lord of Harvest, let there be
  Joy and strength to work for Thee
  Till the nations far and near
  See Thy light and learn Thy fear.

Text: *Jonathan F. Bahnmeier (1774—1841), cento; trans. Catherine Winkworth (1827—78), alt.*
Tune: ***Höchster Priester*** *(Musikalischer Christenschatz, Basel, 1745)*

1 We all be-lieve in one true God, Fa-ther, Son, and Ho-ly Ghost,
2 We all be-lieve in Je - sus Christ, Son of God and Ma-ry's Son,
3 We all con-fess the Ho-ly Ghost, Who from both for-e'er pro-ceeds;

Ev - er - pres - ent Help in need, Praised by all the heav'n - ly host,
Who de-scend-ed from His throne And for us sal - va - tion won;
Who up-holds and com-forts us In all tri - als, fears, and needs.

By whose mighty pow'r a - lone All is made and wrought and done.
By whose cross and death are we Res-cued from all mis - er - y.
Blest and Ho - ly Trin-i - ty, Praise for-ev - er be to Thee! A-men.

Text: *Tobias Clausnitzer (1619—84); trans. Catherine Winkworth (1827—78), alt.*
Tune: ***Wir glauben all' an einen Gott*** *(Kirchengesangbuch, Darmstadt, 1699), adapted*

Open Now Thy Gates of Beauty

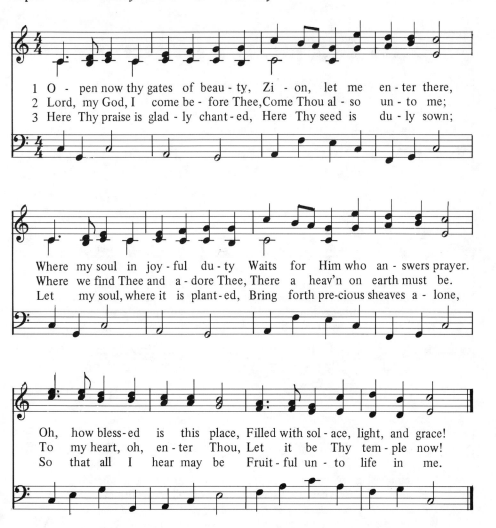

1 O - pen now thy gates of beau - ty, Zi - on, let me en - ter there,
2 Lord, my God, I come be - fore Thee, Come Thou al - so un - to me;
3 Here Thy praise is glad - ly chant - ed, Here Thy seed is du - ly sown;

Where my soul in joy - ful du - ty Waits for Him who an - swers prayer.
Where we find Thee and a - dore Thee, There a heav'n on earth must be.
Let my soul, where it is plant - ed, Bring forth pre - cious sheaves a - lone,

Oh, how bless - ed is this place, Filled with sol - ace, light, and grace!
To my heart, oh, en - ter Thou, Let it be Thy tem - ple now!
So that all I hear may be Fruit - ful un - to life in me.

4 Thou my faith increase and quicken,
Let me keep Thy gift divine,
Howsoe'er temptations thicken;
May Thy Word still o'er me shine
As my guiding star through life,
As my comfort in my strife.

5 Speak, O God, and I will hear Thee,
Let Thy will be done indeed;
May I undisturbed draw near Thee
While Thou dost Thy people feed.
Here of life the fountain flows,
Here is balm for all our woes.

Text: Benjamin Schmolck (1672—1737), cento; trans. Catherine Winkworth (1827—78), alt.
*Tune: **Neander**, Joachim Neander (1650—80)*

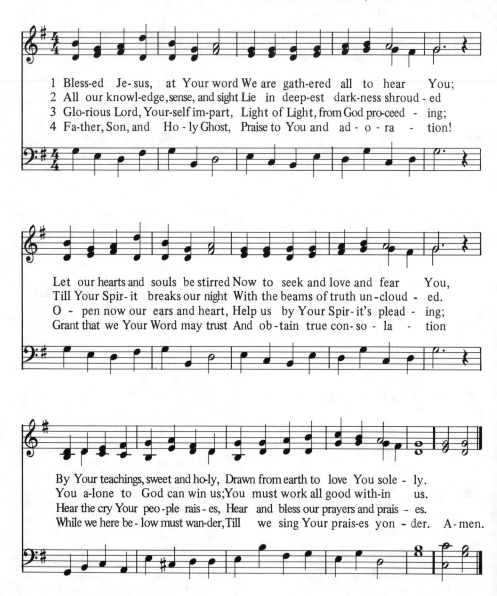

1 Bless-ed Je-sus, at Your word We are gath-ered all to hear You;
2 All our knowl-edge, sense, and sight Lie in deep-est dark-ness shroud - ed
3 Glo-rious Lord, Your-self im-part, Light of Light, from God pro-ceed - ing;
4 Fa-ther, Son, and Ho - ly Ghost, Praise to You and ad - o - ra - tion!

Let our hearts and souls be stirred Now to seek and love and fear You,
Till Your Spir- it breaks our night With the beams of truth un -cloud - ed.
O - pen now our ears and heart, Help us by Your Spir-it's plead - ing;
Grant that we Your Word may trust And ob -tain true con- so - la - tion

By Your teachings, sweet and ho-ly, Drawn from earth to love You sole - ly.
You a-lone to God can win us; You must work all good with-in us.
Hear the cry Your peo-ple rais- es, Hear and bless our prayers and prais - es.
While we here be - low must wan-der, Till we sing Your prais-es yon - der. A - men.

Text: St. 1—3, Tobias Clausnitzer (1616—84), st. 4 anonymous (Berliner Gesangbuch, *1707);
     trans. st. 1—3, Catherine Winkworth (1827—78), alt.; st. 4, unknown.*
*Tune: **Liebster Jesu,** Johann R. Ahle (1625—73)*

1 Fa - ther, we praise You, now the night is o - ver; Ac - tive and
2 Mon - arch of all things, fit us for Your man - sions; Ban - ish our
3 All - ho- ly Fa - ther, Son, and e - qual Spir - it, Trin - i - ty

watch-ful, stand we all be - fore You; Sing - ing we of - fer
weak-ness, health and whole-ness send - ing; Bring us to heav - en,
bless - ed, send us Your sal - va - tion; Yours is the glo - ry,

prayer and med - i - ta - tion; Thus we a - dore You.
where Your saints u - nit - ed Joy with-out end - ing.
gleam - ing and re- sound- ing Through all cre - a - tion. A - men.

Text: Ascr. Gregory the Great (540—604); trans. Percy Dearmer (1876–1936)
Tune: *Christe sanctorum* (La Feillée, Méthode du plain-chant, 1782)
Setting: Carl Schalk (1929—)

1 Lord, dis-miss us with Your bless-ing, Fill our hearts with
2 Thanks we give and ad - o - ra - tion For Your Gos - pel's

joy and peace.   Let us each, Your love pos - sess - ing,
joy - ful sound.   May the fruits of Your sal - va - tion

Tri - umph in re - deem - ing grace. Oh, re - fresh us,
In our hearts and lives a - bound; Ev - er faith - ful,

Oh, re - fresh us, Trav - 'ling through this wil - der - ness!
Ev - er faith - ful To the truth may we be found!

Text: *John Fawcett (1740—1817), cento, alt.*
Tune: **Regent Square,** *Henry Thomas Smart (1813—79)*

1 Savior, a - gain to Thy dear name we raise
2 Grant us Thy peace up - on our home-ward way;
3 Grant us Thy peace, Lord, through the com - ing night;

With one ac - cord our part - ing hymn of praise;
With Thee be - gan, with Thee shall end the day;
Turn Thou for us its dark - ness in - to light.

Once more we bless Thee ere our wor - ship cease,
Guard Thou the lips from sin, the hearts from shame,
From harm and dan - ger keep Thy chil - dren free;

Then, low - ly bend - ing, wait Thy word of peace.
That in this house have called up - on Thy name.
For dark and light are both a - like to Thee.

Text: John Ellerton (1826—93), cento
Tune: *Ellers*, Edward J. Hopkins (1818—1901)

1 Let   there   be peace   on   earth   And   let   it   be -
2 Let   peace   be - gin   with me,   Let   this be the

gin   with me; _____   Let   there be   peace on
mo - ment now. _____   With   ev - 'ry step   I

earth, The peace that was meant to   be. _____   With God
take, Let this be my sol - emn vow: _____   To

as   our Fa - ther, _____   Broth - ers all   are we. _____

Text: Sy Miller and Jill Jackson
Tune: Sy Miller and Jill Jackson
Setting: Carl Streufert

1 Sent forth by God's bless-ing, Our true faith con-fess-ing, The peo-ple of
2 With praise and thanks-giv-ing To God ev-er-liv-ing, The tasks of our

God from His dwell-ing take leave. The serv-ice is end-ed. Oh,
ev-'ry-day life we will face. Our faith ev-er shar-ing, In

now be ex-tend-ed The fruits of this serv-ice in all who be-lieve.
love ev-er car-ing, Em-brac-ing as broth-ers all men of each race.

The seed of His teach-ing, Our hun-gry souls reach-ing, Shall blos-som in
One feast that has fed us, One light that has led us U-nite us as

ac-tion for God and for man. His grace shall in-cite us, His
one in His life that we share. Then may all the liv-ing With

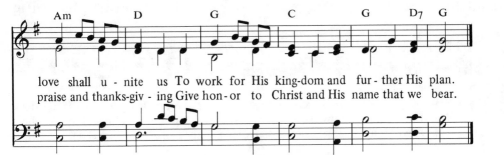

love shall u - nite us To work for His king-dom and fur - ther His plan.
praise and thanks-giv - ing Give hon - or to Christ and His name that we bear.

Text: *Omer Westendorf (1916—), alt.*
Tune: **Ashgrove** *(traditional Welsh melody)*

Shalom, My Friends 127

Sha - lom, my friends! Sha - lom, my friends! Sha - lom! Sha - lom!

His peace be with you! His peace be with you! Sha - lom! Sha - lom!

Text: *Traditional Israeli canon; trans. Theodore Wuerffel (1944—)*
Tune: **Shalom, chaverim** *(traditional Israeli canon)*

1 Je - sus,   Je - sus,   Je - sus in the morn-ing, Je - sus at the
2 Love Him,   Love Him,   Love Him in the morn-ing, Love Him at the
3 Serve Him,   Serve Him,   Serve Him in the morn-ing, Serve Him at the

noon-time, Je - sus,   Je - sus,   Je - sus when the sun goes down.
noon-time, Love Him,   Love Him,   Love Him when the sun goes down.
noon-time, Serve Him,   Serve Him,   Serve Him when the sun goes down.

4 Thank Him

5 Praise Him

Text: Traditional
Tune: Jesus in the morning

It's a glorious feeling to be able
    to unload my heart,
    to spill out my gratitude
        in thanks to You, O God.
Morning, noon, and night
    I want the whole world to know of Your love.
I want to shout it, to sing it,
    in every possible way
        to proclaim Your praises,
        to express my joy.

(Psalm 92)

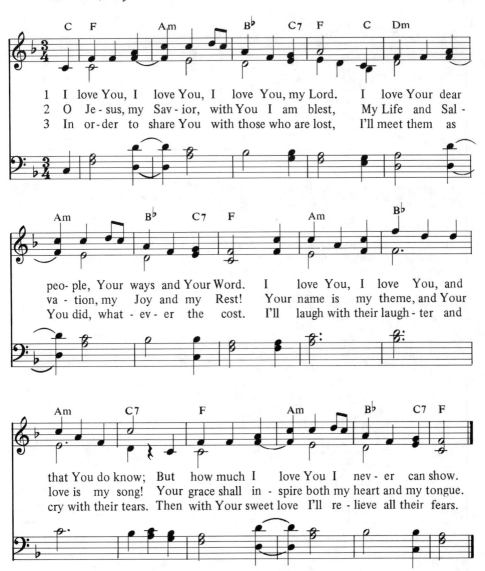

peo-ple, Your ways and Your Word. I love You, I love You, and
va-tion, my Joy and my Rest! Your name is my theme, and Your
You did, what-ev-er the cost. I'll laugh with their laugh-ter and

that You do know; But how much I love You I nev-er can show.
love is my song! Your grace shall in-spire both my heart and my tongue.
cry with their tears. Then with Your sweet love I'll re-lieve all their fears.

Text: St. 1 and 2, anonymous *(Christian Harmony, 1805), alt.; st. 3, Carol Greene (1942—)*
Tune: **Charity** *(Christian Harmony, 1805)*
Setting: Charles Ore (1936—)

1 I've got the joy, joy, joy, joy down in my heart,
2 I've got the love of Je - sus, love of Je - sus down in my heart,
3 I've got the peace that pass - es un - der - stand - ing down in my heart,
4 I've got the joy, joy, joy, joy down in my heart,

Down in my heart, down in my heart! I've got the joy, joy, joy,
Down in my heart, down in my heart! I've got the love of Je - sus, love of
Down in my heart, down in my heart! I've got the peace that pass - es un - der -
Down in my heart, down in my heart! I've got the joy, joy, joy,

joy down in my heart, Down in my heart to stay!
Je - sus down in my heart, Down in my heart to stay!
stand - ing down in my heart, Down in my heart to stay!
joy down in my heart, Down in my heart to stay!   And it's the

great - est, grand - est feel - ing, And it's a feel - ing here to stay!   And it's a

joy that needs re - veal - ing,   So I just want to say:
love
peace

Text: Traditional
Tune: **Joy down in my heart** (traditional)

1 Sing them o-ver a-gain to me, Won-der-ful words of life;
2 Christ, the bless-ed One, gives to all Won-der-ful words of life;
3 Sweet-ly ech-o the Gos-pel call, Won-der-ful words of life;

Let me more of their beau-ty see, Won-der-ful words of life.
Sin-ner, list to the lov-ing call, Won-der-ful words of life.
Of-fer par-don and peace to all, Won-der-ful words of life.

Words of life and beau-ty, Teach me faith and du-ty:
All so free-ly giv-en, Woo-ing us to heav-en:
Je-sus, on-ly Sav-ior, Sanc-ti-fy for-ev-er:

Refrain

Beau-ti-ful words, won-der-ful words, Won-der-ful words of life;

Beau-ti-ful words, won-der-ful words, Won-der-ful words of life.

Text: Philip P. Bliss (1838—76)
*Tune: **Words of life**, Philip P. Bliss (1838—76)*

1 Thee will I love, my Strength, my Tow - er; Thee will I love, my
Hope, my Joy; Thee will I love with all my pow - er, With ar- dor time shall
ne'er de-stroy. Thee will I love, O Light Di-vine, So long as life is mine.

2 Thee will I love, my Life, my Sav - ior, Who art my best and
tru- est Friend. Thee will I love and praise for- ev - er, For nev-er shall Thy
kind-ness end; Thee will I love with all my heart, Thou my Re-deem-er art.

3 I thank Thee, Je - sus, Sun from heav - en, Whose ra-diance hath bro't
light to me; I thank Thee, who hast rich-ly giv - en All that could make me
glad and free; I thank Thee that my soul is healed By what Thy lips re - vealed.

4 Oh, teach me, Lord, to love Thee truly
With soul and body, head and heart,
And grant me grace that I may duly
Practice fore'er love's sacred art.
Grant that my every thought may be
Directed e'er to Thee.

5 Thee will I love, my Crown of gladness;
Thee will I love, my God and Lord,
Amid the darkest depths of sadness,
Nor for the hope of high reward —
For Thine own sake, O Light Divine,
So long as life is mine.

Text: *Johann Scheffler (1624—77), cento; trans. Catherine Winkworth (1827—78), alt.*
Tune: **Ich will dich lieben** (Harmonischer Lieder-Schatz, Frankfurt, 1738)

1 Come, Thou al - might - y King, Help us Thy name to sing,
2 Come, Thou In - car - nate Word, Gird on Thy might - y sword,
3 Come, ho - ly Com - fort - er, Thy sa - cred wit - ness bear
4 To the great One in Three E - ter - nal prais - es be

Help us to praise. Fa - ther all - glo - ri - ous, O'er all vic -
Our prayer at - tend. Come and Thy peo - ple bless And give Thy
In this glad hour. Thou, who al - might - y art, Now rule in
Hence ev - er - more! His sov -'reign maj - es - ty May we in

to - ri - ous, Come and reign o - ver us, An - cient of Days.
Word suc - cess; Stab - lish Thy righ - teous-ness, Sav - ior and Friend!
ev - 'ry heart And ne'er from us de - part, Spir - it of Pow'r!
glo - ry see And to e - ter - ni - ty Love and a - dore! A - men.

Text: Anonymous (c.1757), cento
*Tune: **Italian Hymn**, Felice de Giardini (1716—96)*

1 My Shep - herd will sup - ply my need; Je - ho - vah is His name:
2 When I walk through the shades of death, Thy pres - ence is my stay;
3 The sure pro - vi - sions of my God At - tend me all my days;

In pas - tures fresh He makes me feed, Be - side the liv - ing stream.
One word of Thy sup-port - ing breath Drives all my fears a - way.
Oh, may Thy house be my a - bode, And all my work be praise.

He brings my wan-d'ring spir - it back When I for - sake His ways
Thy hand, in sight of all my foes, Doth still my ta - ble spread;
There would I find a set - tled rest While oth - ers go and come;

And leads me, for His mer - cy's sake, In paths of truth and grace.
My cup with bless-ings o - ver - flows, Thine oil a - noints my head.
No more a stran - ger, nor a guest, But like a child at home.

Text: Isaac Watts (1674—1748)
*Tune: **Resignation** (early American folk hymn melody; Southern Harmony, 1854)*

1 Sav-ior, like a shep-herd lead us, Much we need Thy ten-der care;
2 We are Thine, do Thou be-friend us, Be the guard-ian of our way;
3 Thou hast prom-ised to re-ceive us, Poor and sin-ful tho' we be;
4 Ear-ly let us seek Thy fa-vor, Ear-ly let us do Thy will;

In Thy pleas-ant pas-tures feed us, For our use Thy folds pre-pare:
Keep Thy flock, from sin de-fend us, Seek us when we go a-stray:
Thou hast mer-cy to re-lieve us, Grace to cleanse, and pow'r to free:
Bless-ed Lord and on-ly Sav-ior, With Thy love our bos-oms fill:

Bless-ed Je-sus, bless-ed Je-sus! Thou hast bought us, Thine we are,
Bless-ed Je-sus, bless-ed Je-sus! Hear, oh, hear us, when we pray;
Bless-ed Je-sus, bless-ed Je-sus! We will ear-ly turn to Thee,
Bless-ed Je-sus, bless-ed Je-sus! Thou hast loved us, love us still,

Bless-ed Je-sus, bless-ed Je-sus! Thou hast bought us, Thine we are.
Bless-ed Je-sus, bless-ed Je-sus! Hear, oh, hear us, when we pray.
Bless-ed Je-sus, bless-ed Je-sus! We will ear-ly turn to Thee.
Bless-ed Je-sus, bless-ed Je-sus! Thou hast loved us, love us still.

Text: Ascr. Dorothy Ann Thrupp (1779—1847)
Tune: Nettleton (traditional American folk hymn; John Wyeth's Repository of Sacred Music, 1813)

1 Je - sus, Sav - ior, pi - lot me   O - ver life's tem-pes-tuous sea;
2 As   a   moth - er   stills her child, Thou canst hush the o - cean wild;
3 When at last   I   near the shore And the fear - ful break-ers roar

Un-known waves be-fore me roll,   Hid - ing rock and treach-'rous shoal.
Bois-t'rous waves o - bey Thy will When Thou say'st to them, "Be still!"
'Twixt me and the peace-ful rest,   Then, while lean - ing on Thy breast,

Chart and com - pass come from Thee: Je - sus, Sav - ior, pi - lot   me.
Won-drous Sov -'reign of   the sea, Je - sus, Sav - ior, pi - lot   me.
May   I   hear Thee say   to me, "Fear not, I   will pi - lot   thee."

Text: Edward Hopper (1818—88), cento
Tune: **Pilot**, John E. Gould (1822—75)

137   When We Walk with the Lord

1 When we walk with the   Lord   In the   light of   His   Word,
2 Not   a   shad - ow can   rise,   Not a   cloud in   the   skies,
3 Not   a   bur - den we   bear,   Not a   sor - row we   share,

What a glo-ry He sheds on our way! While we do His good
But His smile quick-ly drives it a - way; Not a doubt nor a
But our toil He doth rich-ly re - pay; Not a grief nor a

will He a - bides with us still, And with all who will
fear, Not a sigh nor a tear Can a - bide while we
loss, Not a frown nor a cross But is blest if we

Refrain

trust and o - bey. Trust and o - bey, For there's no oth - er

way To be hap - py in Je - sus But to trust and o - bey.

4 But we never can prove
The delights of His love
Until all on the altar we lay;
For the favor He shows
And the joy He bestows
Are for them who will trust and obey.
Refrain

5 Then in fellowship sweet
We will sit at His feet,
Or we'll walk by His side in the way;
What He says we will do,
Where He sends we will go.
Never fear, only trust and obey.
Refrain

Text: *John H. Sammis (1846—1919)*
Tune: **Trust and obey**, *Daniel B. Towner (1850—1919)*

1 Chil - dren of the heav'n - ly Fa - ther   Safe - ly in His bos - om gath - er;   Nest - ling bird nor star in heav - en   Such a ref - uge e'er was giv - en.

2 God His own doth tend and nour - ish;   In His ho - ly courts they flour - ish.   From all e - vil things He spares them,   In His might - y arms He bears them.

3 Nei - ther life nor death shall ev - er   From the Lord His chil - dren sev - er;   Un - to them His grace He show - eth,   And their sor - rows all He know - eth.

4 Tho' He giv - eth or He tak - eth,   God His chil - dren ne'er for - sak - eth.   His the lov - ing pur - pose sole - ly   To pre - serve them pure and ho - ly.

Text: Caroline V. Sandell Berg (1832—1908), cento; trans. Ernst William Olson (1870—1958)
*Tune: **Sandell** (traditional Swedish melody)*
Setting: Ted Wuerffel (1944—)

1 He's got the whole world in His hands, He's got the
2 He's got the wind and the rain in His hands, He's got the
3 He's got the ti - ny lit- tle ba - by in His hands, He's got the
4 He's got you and me, broth-er, in His hands, He's got

whole wide world in His hands, He's got the whole
sun and the moon in His hands, He's got the wind and the
ti - ny lit - tle ba - by in His hands, He's got the ti - ny lit - tle
you and me, sis - ter, in His hands, He's got you and me,

world in His hands, He's got the whole world in His hands.
rain in His hands, He's got the whole world in His hands.
ba - by in His hands, He's got the whole world in His hands.
broth-er, in His hands, He's got the whole world in His hands.

Text: *American spiritual*
Tune: ***In His hands*** *(American spiritual)*

1 What God or-dains is al-ways good; His will a-bid-eth ho-ly.
2 What God or-dains is al-ways good. He is my Friend and Fa-ther;
3 What God or-dains is al-ways good. This truth re-mains un-shak-en.

As He di-rects my life for me, I fol-low meek and low-ly.
He suf-fers naught to do me harm, Tho' man-y storms may gath-er.
Tho' sor-row, need, or death be mine, I shall not be for-sak-en.

My God in-deed In ev-'ry need Doth well know how to
Now I may know Both joy and woe, Some day I shall see
I fear no harm, For with His arm He shall em-brace and

shield me; To Him, then, I will yield me.
clear-ly That He hath loved me dear-ly.
shield me; So to my God I yield me.

Text: Samuel Rodigast (1649—1708); trans. composite (The Lutheran Hymnal, *1940*)
Tune: **Was Gott tut,** *Severus Gastorius (17th century)*

1 Oh, that the Lord would guide my ways To keep His stat - utes still!
2 Or - der my foot - steps by Thy Word, And make my heart sin - cere;
3 As - sist my soul, too apt to stray, A strict-er watch to keep;
4 Make me to walk in Thy commands—'Tis a de-light - ful road—

Oh, that my God would grant me grace To know and do His will!
Let sin have no do - min- ion, Lord, But keep my con-science clear.
And should I e'er for - get Thy way, Re - store Thy wan-d'ring sheep.
Nor let my head or heart or hands Of - fend a - gainst my God.

Text: Isaac Watts (1674—1748), cento, alt.
Tune: Evan, William H. Havergal (1793—1870)

I love You, O God,
    and I gladly accept Your will and purpose
      for my life.
Now bless me and guide me
    and grant me the grace
      to walk within that will and purpose
      and have the joy of knowing
        that I am pleasing to You.
                    (Psalm 119)

1 Oh, take my hand, dear Fa - ther, And lead Thou me
2 Oh, cov - er with Thy mer - cy My poor, weak heart
3 Tho' oft Thy pow'r but faint - ly May stir my soul,

Till at my jour- ney's end - ing I dwell with Thee.
Lest I in joy or sor - row From Thee de - part.
With Thee, my Light in dark - ness, I reach the goal.

A - lone I can - not wan - der One sin - gle day;
Per - mit Thy child to lin - ger Here at Thy feet,
Take then my hand, dear Fa - ther, And lead Thou me

So do Thou guide my foot - steps On life's rough way.
Thy good - ness blind - ly trust - ing With faith com - plete.
Till at my jour - ney's end - ing I dwell with Thee.

Text: *Julia Hausmann (1825—1901); trans. Herman Brueckner (1866—1942)*
Tune: **So nimm denn meine Hände,** *Friedrich Silcher (1789—1860)*

Text: *Sigismund von Birken (1626—81), cento; trans. J. Adam Rimbach (1871—1941)*
Tune: ***Lasset uns mit Jesu ziehen**, Georg G. Boltze (18th century)*

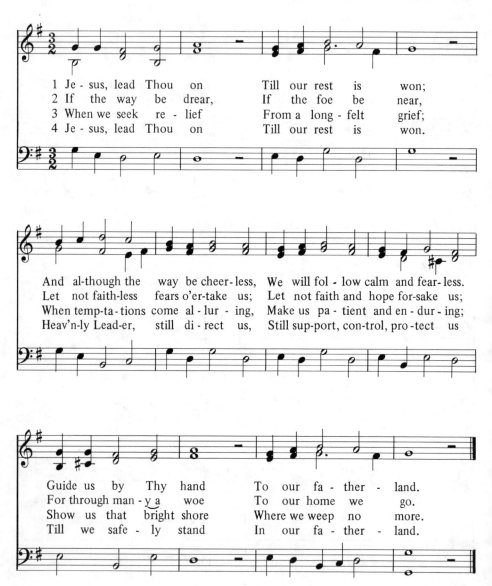

1 Je - sus, lead Thou on   Till our rest is won;
2 If the way be drear,   If the foe be near,
3 When we seek re - lief   From a long - felt grief;
4 Je - sus, lead Thou on   Till our rest is won.

And al-though the way be cheer-less,   We will fol - low calm and fear-less,
Let not faith-less fears o'er-take us;   Let not faith and hope for-sake us;
When temp-ta-tions come al - lur - ing,   Make us pa - tient and en - dur-ing;
Heav'n-ly Lead-er, still di - rect us,   Still sup-port, con-trol, pro - tect us

Guide us by Thy hand   To our fa - ther - land.
For through man - y a woe   To our home we go.
Show us that bright shore   Where we weep no more.
Till we safe - ly stand   In our fa - ther - land.

Text: Nicholas Ludwig von Zinzendorf (1700—60), cento; trans. Jane Borthwick (1813—97), alt.
Tune: Seelenbräutigam, Adam Drese (1620—1701)

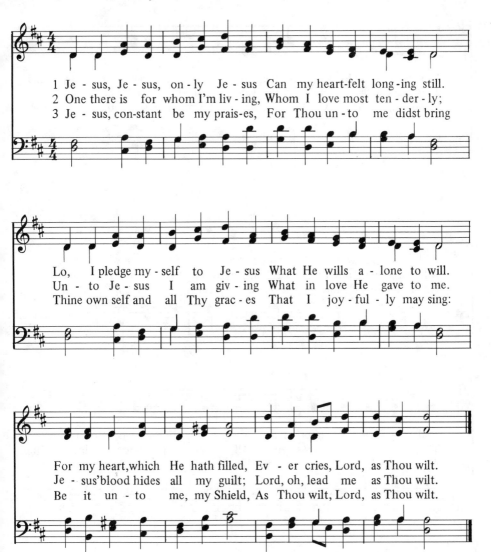

1 Je - sus, Je - sus, on - ly Je - sus Can my heart-felt long -ing still.
2 One there is for whom I'm liv - ing, Whom I love most ten - der - ly;
3 Je - sus, con-stant be my prais-es, For Thou un - to me didst bring

Lo, I pledge my - self to Je - sus What He wills a - lone to will.
Un - to Je - sus I am giv - ing What in love He gave to me.
Thine own self and all Thy grac - es That I joy - ful - ly may sing:

For my heart, which He hath filled, Ev - er cries, Lord, as Thou wilt.
Je - sus' blood hides all my guilt; Lord, oh, lead me as Thou wilt.
Be it un - to me, my Shield, As Thou wilt, Lord, as Thou wilt.

Text: *Ludämilia Elisabeth (1640—72), cento; trans. August Crull (1846—1923), alt.*
Tune: **Jesus, Jesus, nichts als Jesus** (Vollkommenes Choral-Buch, *Hamburg, 1715)*

1 I walk with Je - sus all the way, His guid-ance nev - er fails me;
2 I walk with an - gels all the way, They shield me and be - friend me;
3 My walk is heav'n-ward all the way; A - wait, my soul, the mor - row,

With - in His wounds I find a stay When Sa-tan's pow'r as - sails me;
All Sa - tan's pow'r is held at bay When heav'n-ly hosts at - tend me;
When you shall find re - lease for aye From all your sin and sor - row.

And by His foot-steps led, My path I safe - ly tread In
They are my sure de - fense, All fear and sor-row, hence! Un -
All world-ly pomp, be - gone! To heav'n I now press on. For

spite of ills that threat-en may, I walk with Je - sus all the way.
harmed by foes, do what they may, I walk with an - gels all the way.
all the world I would not stay; My walk is heav'n-ward all the way.

Text: *Hans A. Brorson (1694—1764), cento; trans. Ditlef G. Ristad (1863—1938), alt.*
Tune: **Der lieben Sonne Licht und Pracht** (Geistreiches Gesangbuch, *Halle, 1704*)

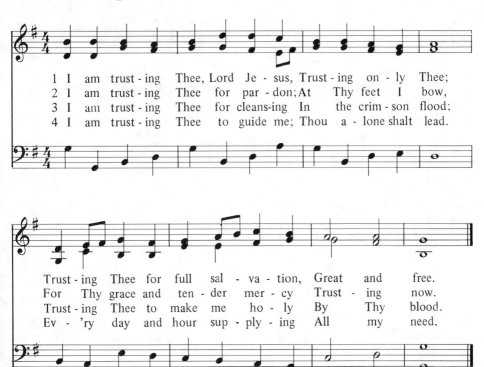

1 I am trust-ing Thee, Lord Je-sus, Trust-ing on-ly Thee;
2 I am trust-ing Thee for par-don; At Thy feet I bow,
3 I am trust-ing Thee for cleans-ing In the crim-son flood;
4 I am trust-ing Thee to guide me; Thou a-lone shalt lead.

Trust-ing Thee for full sal-va-tion, Great and free.
For Thy grace and ten-der mer-cy Trust-ing now.
Trust-ing Thee to make me ho-ly By Thy blood.
Ev-'ry day and hour sup-ply-ing All my need.

5 I am trusting Thee for power;
Thine can never fail.
Words which Thou Thyself shalt give me
Must prevail.

6 I am trusting Thee, Lord Jesus;
Never let me fall.
I am trusting Thee forever
And for all.

Text: Francis R. Havergal (1836—79)
*Tune: **Stephanos**, Henry W. Baker (1821—77)*

1 A might-y for-tress is our God, A sword and shield vic-
2 No strength of ours can match his might! We would be lost, re-
3 Tho' hordes of dev-ils fill the land All threat-'ning to de-
4 God's Word for-ev-er shall a-bide No thanks to foes, who

to - rious, He breaks the cruel op-pres-sor's rod,
ject - ed, But now a cham-pion comes to fight
vour us, We trem-ble not, un-moved we stand;
fear it, For God Him-self fights by our side

And wins sal-va-tion glo - rious. The old e -
Whom God Him-self e-lect - ed. Ask who this
They can-not o-ver-pow'r us. This world's prince
With weap-ons of the Spir - it. If they take

vil foe, Sworn to work us woe, With dread craft and might
may be: Lord of Hosts is He! Je-sus Christ, our Lord,
may rage, In fierce war en-gage, He is doomed to fail;
our house, Goods, fame, child, or spouse, Wrench our life a-way,

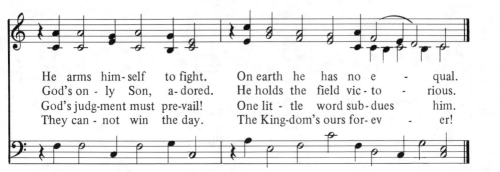

He arms him-self to fight. On earth he has no e - qual.
God's on - ly Son, a- dored. He holds the field vic - to - rious.
God's judg-ment must pre-vail! One lit - tle word sub-dues him.
They can - not win the day. The King-dom's ours for- ev - er!

Text: Martin Luther (1483—1546); trans. composite (Lutheran Book of Worship)
Tune: Ein' feste Burg, Martin Luther (1483—1546)

A Mighty Fortress 149

(Sung to *Ein' feste Burg,* #148)

1 A mighty fortress is our God,
A trusty shield and weapon;
He helps us free from every need
That hath us now o'ertaken.
The old evil foe
Now means deadly woe;
Deep guile and great might
Are his dread arms in fight;
On earth is not his equal.

2 With might of ours can naught be done,
Soon were our loss effected;
But for us fights the Valiant One,
Whom God Himself elected.
Ask ye, Who is this?
Jesus Christ it is,
Of Sabaoth Lord,
And there's none other God;
He holds the field forever.

3 Though devils all the world should fill,
All eager to devour us,
We tremble not, we fear no ill,
They shall not overpower us.
This world's prince may still
Scowl fierce as he will,
He can harm us none,
He's judged; the deed is done;
One little word can fell him.

4 The Word they still shall let remain
Nor any thanks have for it;
He's by our side upon the plain
With His good gifts and Spirit.
And take they our life,
Goods, fame, child, and wife;
Let these all be gone,
They yet have nothing won;
The Kingdom ours remaineth.

Text: Martin Luther (1483–1546); trans. composite (The Lutheran Hymnal)
Tune: Ein' feste Burg, Martin Luther (1483—1546)

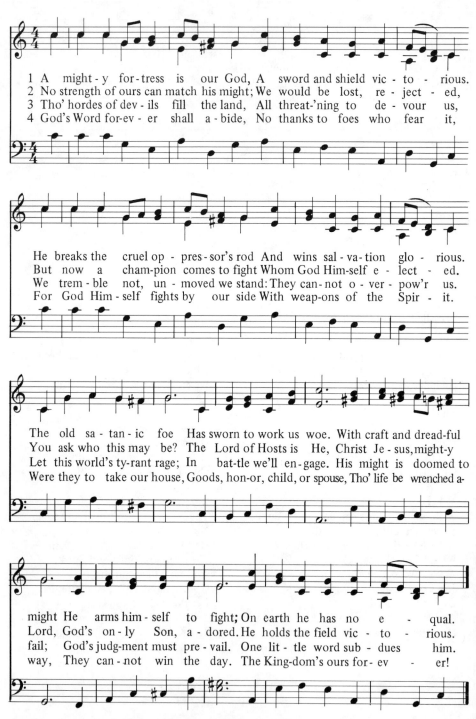

1 A might-y for-tress is our God, A sword and shield vic-to-rious.
2 No strength of ours can match his might; We would be lost, re-ject-ed,
3 Tho' hordes of dev-ils fill the land, All threat-'ning to de-vour us,
4 God's Word for-ev-er shall a-bide, No thanks to foes who fear it,

He breaks the cruel op-pres-sor's rod And wins sal-va-tion glo-rious.
But now a cham-pion comes to fight Whom God Him-self e-lect-ed.
We trem-ble not, un-moved we stand: They can-not o-ver-pow'r us.
For God Him-self fights by our side With weap-ons of the Spir-it.

The old sa-tan-ic foe Has sworn to work us woe. With craft and dread-ful
You ask who this may be? The Lord of Hosts is He, Christ Je-sus, might-y
Let this world's ty-rant rage; In bat-tle we'll en-gage. His might is doomed to
Were they to take our house, Goods, hon-or, child, or spouse, Tho' life be wrenched a-

might He arms him-self to fight; On earth he has no e-qual.
Lord, God's on-ly Son, a-dored. He holds the field vic-to-rious.
fail; God's judg-ment must pre-vail. One lit-tle word sub-dues him.
way, They can-not win the day. The King-dom's ours for-ev-er!

Text: Martin Luther (1483—1546); trans. composite (Lutheran Book of Worship)
Tune: Ein' feste Burg, Martin Luther (1483—1546)

1 All de - pends on our pos - sess - ing God's a - bun - dant
2 Man - y spend their lives in fret - ting O - ver tri - fles
3 When with sor - row I am strick - en, Hope my heart a -
4 Well He knows what best to grant me; All the long - ing

grace and bless - ing, Though all earth - ly wealth de - part.
and in get - ting Things that have no sol - id ground.
new will quick - en, All my long - ing shall be stilled.
hopes that haunt me, Joy and sor - row, have their day.

He who trusts with faith un - shak - en In his God is
I shall strive to win a trea - sure That will bring me
To His lov - ing - kind - ness ten - der Soul and bod - y
I shall doubt His wis - dom nev - er; As God wills, so

not for - sak - en And e'er keeps a daunt - less heart.
last - ing plea - sure And that now is sel - dom found.
I sur - ren - der; For on Him a - lone I build.
be it ev - er; I to Him com - mit my way.

Text: Gesangbuch, *Nürnberg, 1676; trans. Catherine Winkworth (1827—78), alt.*
Tune: **Alles ist an Gottes Segen** *(König's* Harmonischer Lieder-Schatz, *1738)*

1 Take my life and let it be Con-se-crat-ed, Lord, to Thee;
2 Take my hands and let them move At the im-pulse of Thy love;
3 Take my voice and let me sing Al-ways, on-ly, for my King;
4 Take my sil-ver and my gold, Not a mite would I with-hold;

Take my mo-ments and my days, Let them flow in cease-less praise.
Take my feet and let them be Swift and beau-ti-ful for Thee.
Take my lips and let them be Filled with mes-sag-es from Thee.
Take my in-tel-lect and use Ev-'ry pow'r as Thou shalt choose.

5 Take my will and make it Thine,
It shall be no longer mine;
Take my heart, it is Thine own,
It shall be Thy royal throne.

6 Take my love, my Lord, I pour
At Thy feet its treasure-store;
Take myself, and I will be
Ever, only, all for Thee.

Text: Francis R. Havergal (1836—79)
Tune: **Patmos**, *William H. Havergal (1793—1870)*

1 Let me learn of Je - sus; He is kind to me;
2 When I go to Je - sus, He will hear me pray,
3 Let me think of Je - sus; He is full of love,

Once He died to save me, Nailed up - on the tree.
Make me pure and ho - ly, Take my sins a - way.
Look - ing down up - on me From His throne a - bove.

4 If I trust in Jesus,
  If I do His will,
  Then I shall be happy,
  Safe from every ill.

5 Oh, how good is Jesus!
  May He hold my hand
  And at last receive me
  To a better land.

Text: Fanny J. Crosby (1820—1915)
*Tune: **Sandown**, James Frederick Swift (1847—1931)*

My Faith Looks Up to Thee   154

1 My faith looks up to Thee, Thou Lamb of Cal - va - ry,
2 May Thy rich grace im - part Strength to my faint - ing heart,

Sav - ior di - vine. Now hear me while I pray; Take all my
My zeal in - spire! As Thou hast died for me, Oh, may my

guilt a - way; Oh, let me from this day Be whol - ly Thine!
love to Thee Pure, warm, and changeless be, A liv - ing fire! A - men.

Text: Ray Palmer (1808—87), cento
*Tune: **Olivet**, Lowell Mason (1792—1872)*

Text: *American spiritual, cento, alt.*
Tune: *I want to be a Christian (American spiritual)*

1 O Je - sus, I have prom - ised To serve Thee to the end;
2 Oh, let me feel Thee near me, The world is ev - er near;
3 O Je - sus, Thou hast prom - ised To all who fol - low Thee

Be Thou for - ev - er near me, My Mas - ter and my Friend;
I see the sights that daz - zle, The tempt-ing sounds I hear.
That where Thou art in glo - ry There shall Thy ser - vant be;

I shall not fear the bat - tle If Thou art by my side,
My foes are ev - er near me, A - round me and with - in;
And, Je - sus, I have prom - ised To serve Thee to the end;

Nor wan-der from the path - way If Thou wilt be my Guide.
But, Je - sus, draw Thou near - er, And shield my soul from sin.
Oh, give me grace to fol - low, My Sav - ior and my Friend.

Text: *John E. Bode (1816—74)*
Tune: ***Llanfyllin*** *(traditional Welsh melody)*

1 Have Thine own way, Lord! Have Thine own way! Thou art the Pot-ter, I am the clay. Mold me and make me af-ter Thy will, While I am wait-ing yield-ed and still.

2 Have Thine own way, Lord! Have Thine own way! Search me and try me, Mas-ter, to-day! Whit-er than snow, Lord, wash me just now As in Thy pres-ence hum-bly I bow.

3 Have Thine own way, Lord! Have Thine own way! Wound-ed and wea-ry, help me, I pray! Pow-er, all pow-er sure-ly is Thine! Touch me and heal me, Sav-ior di-vine!

4 Have Thine own way, Lord! Have Thine own way! Hold o'er my be-ing ab-so-lute sway! Fill with Thy Spir-it till all shall see Christ on-ly, al-ways, liv-ing in me!

Text: Adelaide A. Pollard (1862—1934)
Tune: Pollard, George C. Stebbins (1846—1945)

1 Just as I am, with-out one plea But that Thy
2 Just as I am, though tossed a - bout With man - y a
3 Just as I am, Thou wilt re - ceive, Wilt wel - come,
4 Just as I am, Thy love un - known Has bro - ken

blood was shed for me And that Thou bidd'st me
con - flict, man - y a doubt, Fight - ings and fears with -
par - don, cleanse, re - lieve; Be - cause Thy prom - ise
ev - 'ry bar - rier down. Now to be Thine, yea,

come to Thee, O Lamb of God, I come, I come.
in, with - out, O Lamb of God, I come, I come.
I be - lieve, O Lamb of God, I come, I come.
Thine a - lone, O Lamb of God, I come, I come.

Text: Charlotte Elliott (1789—1871)
Tune: Woodworth, William B. Bradbury (1816—68)

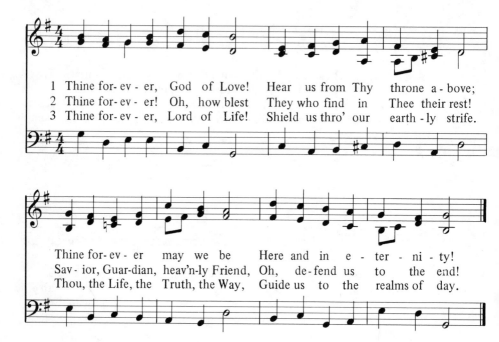

1 Thine for- ev - er, God of Love!   Hear us from Thy   throne a - bove;
2 Thine for- ev - er! Oh, how blest   They who find in   Thee their rest!
3 Thine for- ev - er, Lord of Life!   Shield us thro' our   earth - ly strife.

Thine for- ev - er may we be   Here and in e - ter - ni - ty!
Sav - ior, Guar-dian, heav'n-ly Friend,   Oh, de-fend us to the end!
Thou, the Life, the Truth, the Way,   Guide us to the realms of day.

4 Thine forever! Shepherd, keep
These Thy frail and trembling sheep.
Safe alone beneath Thy care,
Let us all Thy goodness share.

5 Thine forever! Thou our Guide,
All our wants by Thee supplied,
All our sins by Thee forgiven;
Lead us, Lord, from earth to heaven.

Text: Mary F. Maude (1819—87), cento
*Tune: **Vienna,** Justin H. Knecht (1752—1817)*

As for me, my heart waits on God.
I know that my salvation comes from Him.
I may change my views about many things;
    but as for my need for God and His love,
      that is one conviction
       which shall never change.

(Psalm 62)

1 To - day Your mer-cy calls us To wash a - way our sin.
2 To - day Your gate is o - pen, And all who en - ter in
3 To - day our Fa-ther calls us, His Ho - ly Spir - it waits;
4 O all - em - brac-ing Mer - cy, O ev - er - o - pen Door,

How - ev - er great our tres - pass, What-ev - er we have been,
Shall find a Fa - ther's wel - come And par - don for their sin.
His bless-ed an - gels gath - er A - round the heav'n-ly gates.
What should we do with - out You When heart and eye run o'er?

How - ev - er long from mer - cy Our hearts have turned a - way,
The past shall be for - got - ten, A pres - ent joy be giv'n,
No ques-tion will be asked us How of - ten we have come;
When all things seem a - gainst us, To drive us to de - spair,

Your pre - cious blood can cleanse us And make us pure to - day.
A fu - ture grace be prom - ised, A glo-rious crown in heav'n.
Al-though we oft have wan - dered, It is our Fa - ther's home.
We know one gate is o - pen, One ear will hear our prayer.

Text: Oswald Allen (1816—78), cento, alt.
*Tune: **Anthes**, Friedrich K. Anthes (1812— ?)*

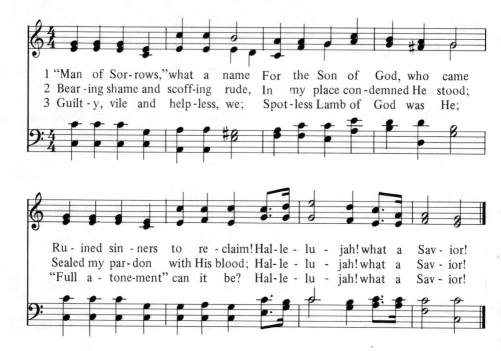

1 "Man of Sor-rows,"what a name For the Son of God, who came
2 Bear-ing shame and scoff-ing rude, In my place con-demned He stood;
3 Guilt-y, vile and help-less, we; Spot-less Lamb of God was He;

Ru-ined sin-ners to re-claim! Hal-le - lu - jah! what a Sav-ior!
Sealed my par-don with His blood; Hal-le - lu - jah! what a Sav-ior!
"Full a-tone-ment" can it be? Hal-le - lu - jah! what a Sav-ior!

4 Lifted up was He to die;
"It is finished," was His cry;
Now in heav'n exalted high;
Hallelujah! what a Savior!

5 When He comes, our glorious King,
All His ransomed home to bring,
Then anew this song we'll sing:
Hallelujah! what a Savior!

Text: Philip P. Bliss (1838—76)
*Tune: **Hallelujah, what a Savior**, Philip P. Bliss (1838—76)*

It's the truth; it's a fact!
We need only to claim it and celebrate it!
We are not to be judged under the Law,
   nor are we to be condemned in our Lawbreaking.
When we accept what God has done for us through Christ,
   we are delivered completely and forever
    from the guilt of sin.
It is just as if sin never happened.
This is what Christ did for us
   some two thousand years ago.

(Romans 8)

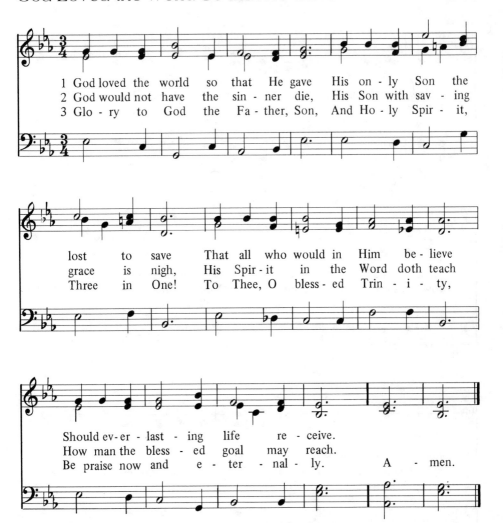

1 God loved the world so that He gave His on-ly Son the
2 God would not have the sin-ner die, His Son with sav-ing
3 Glo-ry to God the Fa-ther, Son, And Ho-ly Spir-it,

lost to save That all who would in Him be-lieve
grace is nigh, His Spir-it in the Word doth teach
Three in One! To Thee, O bless-ed Trin-i-ty,

Should ev-er-last-ing life re-ceive.
How man the bless-ed goal may reach.
Be praise now and e-ter-nal-ly. A-men.

Text: Anonymous (1791), cento; trans. August Crull (1846—1923), alt.
Tune: St. Crispin, George J. Elvey (1816—93)

1 How won-drous and great   Your works, God of praise! How just, King of
2 To   na-tions long dark   Your light shall be shown; Their wor-ship and

saints,   and true are Your ways!   Oh,   who shall not fear You and
vows   shall come to Your throne;   Your truth and Your judg-ments shall

hon-or Your name? You on - ly   are   ho-ly, You   on-ly   su - preme.
spread all a - broad   Till earth's ev -'ry   peo-ple con - fess You their God.

Text: *Henry U. Onderdonk (1789—1858)*
Tune: **Begone, unbelief** *(early American melody)*

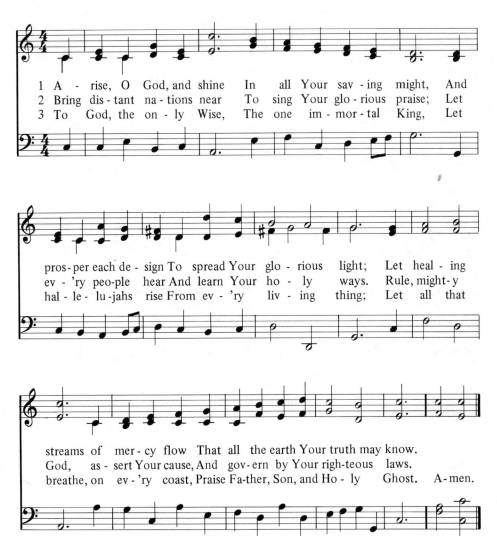

1 A - rise, O God, and shine In all Your sav - ing might, And
2 Bring dis - tant na - tions near To sing Your glo - rious praise; Let
3 To God, the on - ly Wise, The one im - mor - tal King, Let

pros - per each de - sign To spread Your glo - rious light; Let heal - ing
ev - 'ry peo-ple hear And learn Your ho - ly ways. Rule, might-y
hal - le - lu -jahs rise From ev - 'ry liv - ing thing; Let all that

streams of mer - cy flow That all the earth Your truth may know.
God, as - sert Your cause, And gov - ern by Your righ-teous laws.
breathe, on ev - 'ry coast, Praise Fa-ther, Son, and Ho - ly Ghost. A - men.

Text: William Hurn (1754—1829), cento, alt.
Tune: Darwall's 148th, John Darwall (1731—89)

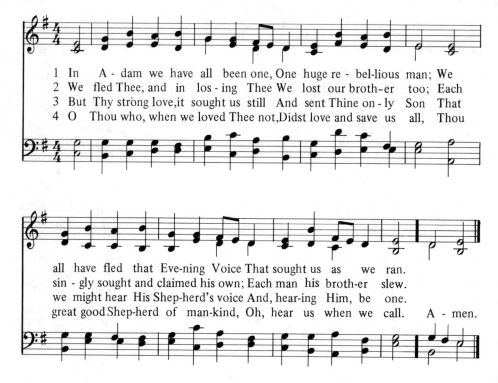

1 In A - dam we have all been one, One huge re - bel-lious man; We
2 We fled Thee, and in los - ing Thee We lost our broth-er too; Each
3 But Thy strong love,it sought us still And sent Thine on - ly Son That
4 O Thou who, when we loved Thee not,Didst love and save us all, Thou

all have fled that Eve-ning Voice That sought us as we ran.
sin - gly sought and claimed his own; Each man his broth-er slew.
we might hear His Shep-herd's voice And, hear-ing Him, be one.
great good Shep-herd of man-kind, Oh, hear us when we call. A - men.

5 Send us thy Spirit, teach us truth;
  Thou Son, oh, set us free
  From fancied wisdom, self-sought ways
  To make us one in Thee.

6 Then shall our song united rise
  To Thine eternal throne,
  Where with the Father evermore
  And Spirit Thou art One.

Text: Martin H. Franzmann (1907—76)
*Tune: **The saints' delight** (Southern Harmony, 1835)*
Setting: Paul Bunjes (1914—)

1 Dear Chris-tians, one and all, re-joice, With ex-ul-ta-tion spring-ing, And with u-nit-ed heart and voice And ho-ly rap-ture sing-ing, Pro-claim the won-ders God has done, How His right arm the vic-t'ry won; Right dear-ly it has cost Him.

2 He spoke to His be-lov-ed Son: 'Tis time to have com-pas-sion. Then go, bright Jew-el of My crown, And bring to man sal-va-tion; From sin and sor-row set him free, Slay bit-ter death for him that he May live with You for-ev-er.

3 The Son o-beyed His Fa-ther's will, Was born of vir-gin moth-er, And God's good plea-sure to ful-fill, He came to be my Broth-er. No garb of pomp or pow'r He wore, A ser-vant's form, like mine, He bore, To lead the dev-il cap-tive.

Text: Martin Luther (1483—1546); trans. Richard Massie (1800—1887), alt., cento
*Tune: **Nun freut euch** (Etlich' christliche Lieder,Wittenberg, 1524)*

Blessed Are the Sons of God

1 Bless-ed are the sons of God, They are bo't with Christ's own blood;
2 They are jus - ti - fied by grace, They en - joy the Sav - ior's peace;
3 They are lights up - on the earth, Chil - dren of a heav'n - ly birth;

They are ran-somed from the grave, Life e - ter - nal they shall have:
All their sins are washed a - way, They shall stand in God's great Day;
One with God, with Je - sus one; Glo - ry is in them be - gun:

With them num-bered may we be Here and in e - ter-ni - ty!
With them num-bered may we be Here and in e - ter-ni - ty!
With them num-bered may we be Here and in e - ter-ni - ty!

Text: Joseph Humphreys (1720— ?), cento, alt.
*Tune: **Voller Wunder**, Johann G. Ebeling (1620—76)*

1 God loves me dear - ly, Grants me sal - va - tion, God loves me
2 I was in slav - 'ry, Sin, death, and dark - ness; God's love was
3 He sent forth Je - sus, My dear Re-deem - er, He sent forth

dear - ly, Loves e - ven me.
work - ing To make me free.   There-fore I'll say a - gain: God
Je - sus And set me free.

loves me dear - ly, God loves me dear - ly, Loves e - ven me.

4 Jesus, my Savior,
  Himself did offer;
  Jesus, my Savior,
  Paid all I owed.

  Refrain

5 Now will I praise You,
  O Love Eternal;
  Now will I praise You
  All my life long.

  Refrain

Text: *August Rische (19th century), cento; trans. composite*
Tune: **Gott ist die Liebe** *(German folk tune)*

It's Me, O Lord

Refrain

It's me, it's me, it's me, O Lord, Stand-ing in the need of prayer;

It's me, it's me, it's me, O Lord, Stand-ing in the need of prayer.

1 Both my broth-er and my sis-ter and it's me, O Lord,
2 Both my fa-ther and my moth-er and it's me, O Lord,
3 Both the preach-er and the dea-con and it's me, O Lord,

Stand-ing in the need of prayer. Both my broth-er and my sis-ter and it's
Stand-ing in the need of prayer. Both my fa-ther and my moth-er and it's
Stand-ing in the need of prayer. Both the preach-er and the dea-con and it's

Text: American spiritual
*Tune: **It's me** (American spiritual)*
Setting: Charles Ore (1936—)

me, O Lord, Stand-ing in the need of prayer.
me, O Lord, Stand-ing in the need of prayer.
me, O Lord, Stand-ing in the need of prayer.

4 Both my neighbor and the stranger and it's me, O Lord. *Refrain*
5 Both _____ and _____ and it's me, O Lord. *Refrain*

All Things Are Thine

170

All things are Thine; no gift have we, Lord of all

gifts, to of - fer Thee; And hence with grate - ful

hearts to - day Thine own be - fore Thy feet we lay.

Text: John Greenleaf Whittier (1807—92), cento
Tune: Germany (William Gardiner's Sacred Melodies, 1815)

1 What a Friend we have in Je - sus, All our sins and griefs to bear!
2 Have we tri - als and temp-ta - tions? Is there trou -ble an - y - where?
3 Are we weak and heav-y la - den, Cum-bered with a load of care?

What a priv - i - lege to car - ry Ev - 'ry-thing to God in prayer!
We should nev-er be dis - cour-aged, Take it to the Lord in prayer.
Pre - cious Sav -ior, still our Ref-uge; Take it to the Lord in prayer.

Oh, what peace we of - ten for - feit, Oh, what need-less pain we bear,
Can we find a Friend so faith - ful Who will all our sor- rows share?
Do thy friends de-spise, for-sake thee? Take it to the Lord in prayer;

All be-cause we do not car - ry Ev - 'ry-thing to God in prayer!
Je - sus knows our ev -'ry weak - ness; Take it to the Lord in prayer.
In His arms He'll take and shield thee; Thou wilt find a sol-ace there.

Text: Joseph Scriven (1820—86)
*Tune: **Converse**, Charles Crozat Converse (1832—1918)*

```
1          Our      Fa - ther   who art   in heav - en,
2          As    in heav - en,  so   on   the earth;
3  And for - give us,  Fa - ther,  all  our  debts,
4  And      lead us   not  in - to  temp - ta - tion,
5  For      Thine is the king - dom,  pow - er,  and glo - ry,
6  A   -    men,  a  - men,  it   shall be  so,
```

Hal - low - ed   be   Thy   name;

```
1  Thy     king - dom  come,    Thy  will  be    done,
2  Give    us    this  day      our  dai - ly    bread;
3  As      we    for - give         all  our    debt - ors.
4  But de - liv - er   us       from all         e - vil.
5  For  -  ev  - er    and      for - ev - er and ev - er.
6  A   -   men,  a  -  men,     it   shall be    so.
```

Hal - low - ed   be   Thy   name.

These chords can be used to improvise your own piano accompaniment:

Text: Matthew 6:9-13; adapted, Ewald Bash (1924—)
*Tune: **Hallowed be thy name** (West Indies folk melody)*

1 O   Thou, who hast of Thy pure grace   Made   shine on us   a
2 O   King and Fa - ther, kind and dread,   Give   us this day our
3 Thine is the King-dom, un - to Thee   Shall   bow in hom - age

Fa - ther's face,   A -   rise, Thy ho - ly   name make known;
dai - ly bread;   For -   give us, who have learned to bless
ev - 'ry knee;   And   Thine the pow'r; no pow'r shall be

Take   up Thy pow'r and reign a - lone;   On   earth, in us, let
Our   en - e-mies, all tres-pass-es;   Spare   us temp - ta - tion,
That   is not o - ver-come by Thee;   The   glo - ry Thine, by

Thy sole will   Be   done as an-gels do it still.
let us be   From Sa - tan set for - ev - er free.
ev-'ry tongue Thy praise shall be for-ev - er sung.   A -   men.

Text: Martin H. Franzmann (1907—76)
*Tune: **Vater unser** (Geistliche Lieder, Leipzig, 1539)*
Setting: Paul Bunjes (1914—)

1 Lord of Glo - ry, who hast bo't us With Thy life-blood as the price,
2 Grant us hearts, dear Lord, to yield Thee Glad-ly, free - ly, of Thine own;
3 Lord of Glo - ry, who hast bo't us With Thy life-blood as the price,

Nev - er grudg-ing for the lost ones That tre-men-dous sac - ri - fice;
With the sun - shine of Thy good-ness Melt our thank-less hearts of stone
Nev - er grudg-ing for the lost ones That tre-men-dous sac - ri - fice,

And with that hast free-ly giv - en Bless - ings count-less as the sand
Till our cold and self-ish na - tures, Warmed by Thee, at length be - lieve
Give us faith to trust Thee bold-ly, Hope, to stay our souls on Thee;

To th' un-thank-ful and the e - vil With Thine own un-spar- ing hand;
That more hap - py and more bless-ed 'Tis to give than to re - ceive.
But, oh! best of all Thy grac - es, Give us Thine own char-i - ty.

Text: *Eliza S. (Dykes) Alderson (1818—89)*
Tune: **Hyfrydol,** *Rowland H. Prichard (1811—87), alt.*

1 On - ward, Chris - tian sol - diers, March-ing as to war,
2 Like a might - y ar - my Moves the church of God;
3 Crowns and thrones may per - ish, King-doms rise and wane,
4 On - ward, then, ye faith - ful, Join our hap - py throng,

With the cross of Je - sus Go - ing on be - fore.
Broth - ers, we are tread - ing Where the saints have trod.
But the church of Je - sus Con - stant will re - main.
Blend with ours your voic - es In the tri - umph song:

Christ, the roy - al Mas - ter, Leads a - gainst the foe; For-ward in - to
We are not di - vid - ed, All one bod - y we, One in hope and
Gates of hell can nev - er 'Gainst that church pre-vail; We have Christ's own
Glo - ry, laud, and hon - or Un - to Christ, the King; This thro' count-less

Refrain

bat - tle See His ban-ners go!
doc - trine, One in char - i - ty.
prom - ise, And that can - not fail.   On-ward, Christian sol - diers,
a - ges Men and an - gels sing.

Text: Sabine Baring-Gould (1834—1924), cento
Tune: St. Gertrude, Arthur S. Sullivan (1824—1900)

Marching as to war, With the cross of Je - sus Go-ing on be-fore.

The Church's One Foundation

1 The church's one foun - da - tion Is Je - sus Christ, her Lord;
2 E - lect from ev - 'ry na - tion, Yet one o'er all the earth,

She is His new cre - a - tion By wa - ter and the Word.
Her char - ter of sal - va - tion One Lord, one faith, one birth.

From heav'n He came and sought her To be His ho - ly bride;
One ho - ly name she bless - es, Par - takes one ho - ly food,

With His own blood He bought her, And for her life He died.
And to one hope she press - es, With ev - 'ry grace en - dued.

Text: Samuel J. Stone (1839—1900), cento
Tune: **Aurelia**, Samuel S. Wesley (1810—76)

1 We are climb-ing Ja-cob's lad-der, We are
2 Ev-'ry round goes high-er, high-er, Ev-'ry
3 Sin-ners, do you love your Je-sus? Sin-ners,

climb-ing Ja-cob's lad-der, We are climb-ing
round goes high-er, high-er, Ev-'ry round goes
do you love your Je-sus? Sin-ners, do you

Ja-cob's lad-der, Sol-diers of the cross.
high-er, high-er, Sol-diers of the cross.
love your Je-sus? Sol-diers of the cross.

4   If you love Him, why not serve Him?
5   We are climbing higher, higher.

Text: American spiritual
*Tune: **Jacob's ladder** (American spiritual)*

When Israel Was in Egypt's Land

178

1 When Is-rael was in E-gypt's land, "Let My peo-ple go."
2 "Thus saith the Lord,"bold Mo-ses said, "Let My peo-ple go."
3 "No more shall they in bond-age toil, Let My peo-ple go.
4 Oh, let us all from bond-age flee, "Let My peo-ple go."

Op-prest so hard they could not stand, "Let My peo-ple go."
If not, I'll smite your first-born dead, "Let My peo-ple go."
Let them come out with E-gypt's spoil, Let My peo-ple go."
And let us all in Christ be free, "Let My peo-ple go."

Refrain

Go down, Mo-ses, way down in E-gypt's land,

Tell old Pha-raoh, "Let My peo-ple go."

Text: American spiritual
Tune: **Let my people go** *(American spiritual)*

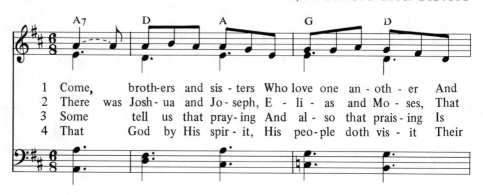

1 Come,   broth-ers and sis - ters Who love one an - oth - er   And
2 There   was Josh- ua and Jo - seph, E - li - as and Mo - ses, That
3 Some   tell   us that pray- ing And al - so that prais- ing Is
4 That   God by His spir - it, His peo-ple doth vis - it Their

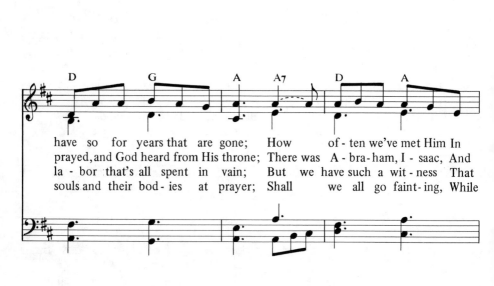

have so for years that are gone;   How   of - ten we've met Him In
prayed,and God heard from His throne; There was A - bra-ham, I - saac, And
la - bor that's all spent in vain;   But   we have such a wit - ness That
souls and their bod - ies   at prayer;   Shall   we all go faint- ing, While

one ho - ly   un - ion, All   sing-ing to God on His throne. With
Ja - cob and Da - vid And   Sol- o- mon, Ste-phen, and John. There was
God hears with swift- ness, From pray-ing we will not re - frain. There was
they go on prais- ing, And   glo - ri - fy God in the   flame? God

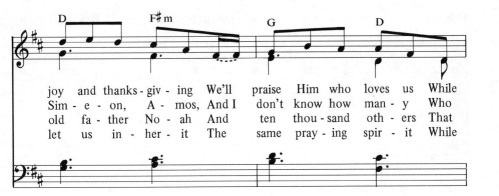

joy and thanks-giv-ing We'll praise Him who loves us While
Sim-e-on, A-mos, And I don't know how man-y Who
old fa-ther No-ah And ten thou-sand oth-ers That
let us in-her-it The same pray-ing spir-it While

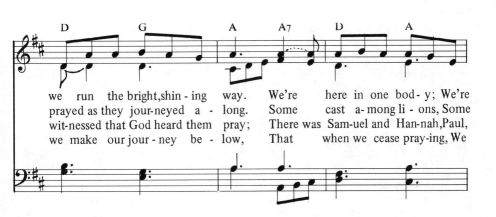

we run the bright,shin-ing way. We're here in one bod-y; We're
prayed as they jour-neyed a-long. Some cast a-mong li-ons, Some
wit-nessed that God heard them pray; There was Sam-uel and Han-nah,Paul,
we make our jour-ney be-low, That when we cease pray-ing, We

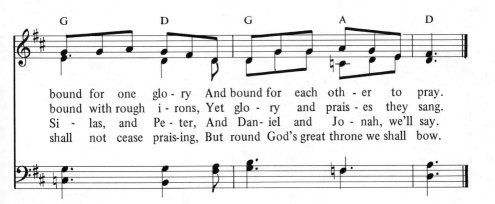

bound for one glo-ry And bound for each oth-er to pray.
bound with rough i-rons, Yet glo-ry and prais-es they sang.
Si-las, and Pe-ter, And Dan-iel and Jo-nah, we'll say.
shall not cease prais-ing, But round God's great throne we shall bow.

Text: American spiritual
Tune: Based on an early American hymn
Setting: Charles Ore (1936—)

Oh, no-bod-y knows the trouble I see, No-bod-y knows but Je-sus;

No-bod-y knows the trou-ble I see, Glo - ry, hal-le-lu - jah!

1 Some-times I'm up, some-times I'm down, Oh, yes, Lord! Some -
2 Al - though you see me going 'long so, Oh, yes, Lord! I
3 What makes old Sa - tan hate me so, Oh, yes, Lord! 'Cause he

times I'm al - most to the ground, Oh, yes, Lord!
have my trou-bles here be - low, Oh, yes, Lord!
got me once and let me go, Oh, yes, Lord!

Text: *American spiritual*
Tune: *Nobody knows (American spiritual)*
Setting: *Norman Lloyd*

D chords: Capo 1

1 Oh, when the saints go march-ing
2 Oh, when they crown Him Lord of

in, Oh, when the saints go march-ing
all, Oh, when they crown Him Lord of

in, O Lord, I want to be in that
all, O Lord, I want to be in that

num-ber When the saints go march-ing in!
num-ber When they crown Him Lord of all.

Text: American spiritual
Tune: American spiritual
Setting: Charles Ore (1936—)

Refrain

Swing low, sweet char - i - ot, Com-ing for to car - ry me home!

Swing low, sweet char - i - ot, Com-ing for to car - ry me home!

1 I looked o - ver Jor - dan, and what did I see,
2 I'm some-times up and some-times down,
Com-ing for to car - ry me home!

A band of an - gels com-ing af-ter me,
But still my soul feels heav-en - ly bound,
Com-ing for to car-ry me home!

Text: American spiritual
Tune: Swing low (American spiritual)

Text: *American spiritual*
Tune: *On my way (American spiritual)*
Setting: *Charles Ore (1936—)*

Refrain

Shout, shout, we are gain-ing ground, Hal-le, hal-le - lu - jah!
Sa - tan's king - dom is tum - bling down, Glo - ry, hal-le - lu - jah!

4 Saint Paul and Silas bound in jail,
Halle, hallelujah!
Would pray and sing in spite of hell;
Glory, hallelujah!
They made the prison loudly ring,
Halle, hallelujah!
Although opposed by hell's dark king.
Glory, hallelujah!

Refrain

5 All glory, glory to the Lamb!
Halle, hallelujah!
Bless, O my soul, His wondrous name.
Glory, hallelujah!
On angel's wings I soon shall rise,
Halle, hallelujah!
And shout His glories in the skies.
Glory, hallelujah!

Refrain

Text: 19th-century revival hymn
*Tune: **Satan's kingdom tumbling** (traditional American melody)*
Setting: Charles Ore (1936—)

1 Oh,   free - dom,   Oh,   free - dom,
2 No   more moan - ing,   No   more moan - ing,
3 There'll be sing - ing, There'll be sing - ing,

Oh,   free - dom o - ver   me!
No   more moan - ing o - ver   me!
There'll be sing - ing o - ver   me!

Refrain
And be - fore I'd be a slave, I'll be bur - ied in my

grave And go home to my Lord and be free.

4 There'll be shouting,
   There'll be shouting,
   There'll be shouting over me!

   Refrain

5 There'll be praying,
   There'll be praying,
   There'll be praying over me!

   Refrain

Text: *American spiritual*
Tune: *Oh, freedom (American spiritual)*
Setting: *Charles Ore (1936—)*

1 Je - ru - sa - lem, my hap - py home, Name
2 A - pos - tles, mar - tyrs, proph - ets, there A -
3 Je - ru - sa - lem, my hap - py home, When
4 O Christ, do Thou my soul pre - pare For

ev - er dear to me, When shall my la - bors
round my Sav - ior stand; And soon my friends in
shall I come to thee? When shall my la - bors
that bright home of love That I may see Thee

have an end? Thy joys when shall I see?
Christ be - low Will join the glo - rious band.
have an end? Thy joys when shall I see?
and a - dore With all Thy saints a - bove.

Text: F.B.P., c. 1580; cento 1801, alt.
*Tune: **Land of Rest** (traditional American folk melody)*

God, Who Made the Earth and Heaven

1 God, who made the earth and heav - en, Dark - ness and light:
2 And when morn a - gain shall call us To run life's way,
3 Ho - ly Fa - ther, throned in heav - en, All - ho - ly Son,

You the day for work have giv - en, For rest the night:
May we still, what - e'er be - fall us, Your will o - bey;
Ho - ly Spir - it, free - ly giv - en, Blest Three in One:

May Your an-gel guards de-fend us, Slum - ber sweet Your mer - cy send us,
From the pow'r of e - vil hide us, In the nar - row path - way guide us,
Grant us grace, we now im-plore You, Till we lay our crowns be-fore You

Ho - ly dreams and hopes at-tend us All through this night.
Nev - er be Your smile de-nied us Each live - long day.
And in wor - thier strains a-dore You While a - ges run. A - men.

Text: *St. 1, Reginald Heber (1783—1826), alt.; st. 2 and 3, William Mercer (1811—73), alt.*
Tune: *Ar hyd y nos (traditional Welsh melody)*
Setting: *Luther O. Emerson (1820—1915)*

1 All praise to Thee, my God, this night For
2 Forgive me, Lord, for Thy dear Son, The
3 Teach me to live that I may dread The
4 Oh, may my soul on Thee repose, And

all the bless-ings of the light; Keep me, oh, keep me,
ill that I this day have done, That with the world, my-
grave as lit-tle as my bed. Teach me to die that
may sweet sleep mine eye-lids close, Sleep that shall me more

King of kings, Be-neath Thine own al-might-y wings!
self, and Thee, I, ere I sleep, at peace may be.
so I may Rise glo-rious at the awe-some day.
vig-'rous make To serve my God when I a-wake! A-men.

5 When in the night I sleepless lie,
My soul with heavenly thoughts
supply;
Let no ill dreams disturb my rest,
No power of darkness me molest.

6 Praise God, from whom all blessings
flow;
Praise Him, all creatures here below;
Praise Him above, ye heavenly host;
Praise Father, Son, and Holy Ghost.

Text: Thomas Ken (1637—1711), cento
*Tune: **Tallis' Canon,** Thomas Tallis (c.1510—85)*

Text: *Henry F. Lyte (1793--1847), cento*
Tune: **Eventide**, *William H. Monk (1823--89)*

1. Sun of my soul, Thou Savior dear, It is not night if Thou be near. Oh, may no earth-born cloud arise To hide Thee from Thy servant's eyes.

2. When the soft dews of kindly sleep My wearied eyelids gently steep, Be my last thought how sweet to rest Forever on my Savior's breast.

3. Abide with me from morn till eve, For without Thee I cannot live; Abide with me when night is nigh, For without Thee I dare not die.

4. If some poor wand'ring child of Thine Has spurned today the voice divine, Now, Lord, the gracious work begin; Let him no more lie down in sin.

5. Watch by the sick; enrich the poor
With blessings from Thy boundless store;
Be every mourner's sleep tonight,
Like infant's slumbers, pure and light.

6. Come near and bless us when we wake,
Ere through the world our way we take,
Till in the ocean of Thy love
We lose ourselves in heaven above.

Text: John Keble (1792—1866), cento
Tune: **Hursley** (Allgemeines Gesangbuch, *Vienna, 1775), adapted*

1 Our Father, by whose name All father-hood is known,
2 O Christ, Thyself a child With-in an earth-ly home,
3 O Spir-it, who dost bind Our hearts in u-ni-ty,

Who dost in love pro-claim Each fam-i-ly Thine own,
With heart still un-de-filed Thou didst to man-hood come;
Who teach-est us to find The love from self set free,

Bless Thou all par-ents, guard-ing well, With con-stant love as
Our chil-dren bless in ev-'ry place That they may all be-
In all our hearts such love in-crease That ev-'ry home, by

sen-ti-nel, The homes in which Thy peo-ple dwell.
hold Thy face And, know-ing Thee, may grow in grace.
this re-lease, May be the dwell-ing place of peace. A-men.

Text: F. Bland Tucker (1895—)
Tune: **Rhosymedre**, John Edwards (1806—85)
Setting: Richard Hillert (1923—)

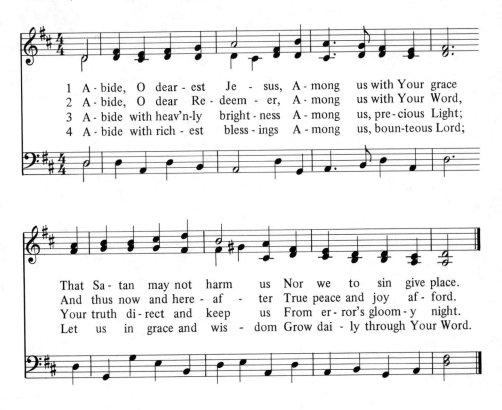

1 A-bide, O dear-est Je - sus, A-mong us with Your grace
2 A-bide, O dear Re - deem - er, A-mong us with Your Word,
3 A-bide with heav'n-ly bright-ness A-mong us, pre-cious Light;
4 A-bide with rich-est bless-ings A-mong us, boun-teous Lord;

That Sa-tan may not harm us Nor we to sin give place.
And thus now and here - af - ter True peace and joy af-ford.
Your truth di-rect and keep us From er-ror's gloom-y night.
Let us in grace and wis - dom Grow dai - ly through Your Word.

5 Abide with Your protection
Among us, Lord, our Strength,
Lest world and Satan fell us
And overcome at length.

6 Abide, O faithful Savior
Among us with Your love;
Grant steadfastness and help us
To reach our home above.

Text: Josua Stegmann (1588—1632); trans. August Crull (1846—1923), alt.
Tune: Christus, der ist mein Leben, Melchior Vulpius (c.1560—1615)

TOPICAL INDEX

He's got the whole world in His
hands 139
How precious is the Book Divine 72
I walk with Jesus all the way 146
Oh, take my hand, dear Father 142
Oh, that the Lord would guide my
ways 141
This is my Father's world 91

HARVEST (See Thanksgiving)

HEAVEN
For all the saints 82
I'm on my way to Canaan land 183
Jerusalem, my happy home 186
Swing low, sweet chariot 182

HOPE
Amazing Grace 80
Come along with me to Bethlehem 11
I'm on my way to Canaan land 183
In Adam we have all been one 165
Let us ever walk with Jesus 143
My faith looks up to Thee 154
Oh, freedom 185
Were you there 39

JESUS (See God)

JOY
Blessed assurance 116
Dear Christians, one and all,
rejoice 166
I've got the joy 130
Oh, freedom 185
Oh, when the saints go marching
in 181
Rejoice, the Lord is King 60
The King shall come when morning
dawns 2
This is a joyous, happy day 76
This is my Father's world 91
This night my soul has caught new
fire 184

LENT
All glory, laud, and honor 41
By Your birth and by Your tears 36
Christ, the Life of all the living 33
Go to dark Gethsemane 35
God loved the world so that He
gave 162
Hosanna, hallelujah 42
"Man of Sorrows," what a name 161
My faith looks up to Thee 154
My song is love unknown 34

O sacred Head, now wounded 45
The King of Glory 40
There is a green hill far away 38
Upon the cross extended 43
Were you there 39
What wondrous love is this 37
When I survey the wondrous cross 44

LOVE: GOD'S LOVE
God loved the world so that He
gave 162
God loves me dearly 168
I love to tell the story 115
In Adam we have all been one 165
My song is love unknown 34
Now the green blade riseth 51
There is a name I love to hear 85
Thy loving kindness 92
What wondrous love is this 37

LOVE: OUR LOVE FOR GOD
I love You, my Lord 129
Jesus in the morning 128
Jesus, Jesus, only Jesus 145
Thee will I love, my Strength, my
Tower 132
There is a name I love to hear 85
We are climbing Jacob's ladder 177

LOVE FOR OTHERS
God of grace and God of glory 113
In Christ there is no East or West 112
Let there be peace on earth 125
Lord of all nations, grant me grace 114
Lord of Glory, who hast bought us 174
Wake us, O Lord, to human need 109
We thank You, Lord, for eyes to
see 111

MERCY
Holy Ghost, with light divine 67
Just as I am 158

MORNING
Father, we praise You 122
God, who made the earth and
heaven 187

NATION (See Patriotism)

NEW YEAR
O God, our help in ages past 29

OBEDIENCE
Blessed assurance 116
Have Thine own way, Lord 157

ALPHABETICAL INDEX OF TUNES

---

*These tunes do not have a tune name. In this index they are included by title.

INDEX OF FIRST LINES
AND COMMON TITLES

ACKNOWLEDGMENTS

The following materials are by permission of Concordia Publishing House: *Worship Supplement* (text-tune and accompaniment editions), Commission on Worship, The Lutheran Church—Missouri Synod, © 1969; *The Parish Organist, Parts I to IV*, Heinrich Fleischer, editor, © 1963; *A Heritage of Hymns* (one-volume edition), Joanna Lange, © 1972.

The numbers listed below refer to the hymns as they appear in *Joyful Sounds*.

Texts from *Worship Supplement:* #5 (trans. of stanza 3), 24 (trans.), 87, 114, 165, 173.

Settings from *Worship Supplement:* #2, 5, 7, 10, 14, 21, 23, 34, 46, 49, 52, 53, 57, 58, 63, 87, 101, 113, 114, 122, 165, 173, 191.

Settings from *The Parish Organist:* #13, 16, 24, 29, 33, 35, 36, 41, 55, 60, 61, 65, 68, 69, 71, 74, 96, 98, 102, 105, 120, 121, 143, 144, 147, 152, 159, 160, 162, 164, 166, 167, 176, 192.

Settings from *A Heritage of Hymns* (altered by permission of Joanna Lange): #45, 47, 64, 88, 148, 149, 174.

The Editorial Committee herewith expresses its gratitude to the persons and institutions named below for their permission to include in *Joyful Sounds* the copyright items listed.

A Mighty Fortress (Rhythmic and Isometric #148 and 150)—Texts reprinted from *Lutheran Book of Worship* by permission of Inter-Lutheran Commission on Worship.

And God Said, Yes! (#93)—Text and tune ("Yes") by permission of Fortress Press.

Beautiful Savior (#81)—Setting for "Schonster Herr Jesu" from *Young Children Sing,* © 1967 by Lutheran Church Press, Philadelphia, and Augsburg Publishing House, Minneapolis. Used by permission.

Child in the Manger (#8)—Text copyright owner untraceable. Setting of **"Bunessan"** from *Carols for the Seasons,* © 1959 by Concordia Publishing House. Used by permission.

Children of the Heavenly Father (#138)—Translation of text from *The Lutheran Service Book and Hymnal* by permission of the Commission on the Liturgy and Hymnal. Setting of "Sandell" by permission of Ted Wuerffel.

Christ the Lord Is Risen Today; Christians (#56)—Setting for "Llanfair" from *Young Children Sing,* © 1967 by Lutheran Church Press, Philadelphia, and Augsburg Publishing House, Minneapolis. Used by permission.

Come Along with Me to Bethlehem (#11)—Text and tune, copyright © 1970 by Frank W. Klos. Used by permission. Setting by permission of R. Harold Terry.

Come Praise the Lord (#94)—Text and tune by permission of World Library Publications, Inc. Setting altered and reprinted with permission of the

Earth and All Stars (#84)—Text and tune ("Earth and All Stars") from *Twelve Folksongs and Spirituals,* © 1968, Augsburg Publishing House; used by permission. Setting reprinted from *Contemporary Worship 1: Hymns,* © 1969, by permission of the publishers for Inter-Lutheran Commission on Worship.

Father, We Praise You (#122)—Text translation by Percy Dearmer from the *English Hymnal* by permission of Oxford University Press.

For All the Saints (#82)—Tune ("Sine nomine") and setting from the *English Hymnal* by permission of Oxford University Press.

From All That Dwell Below the Skies (#83)—Setting of "Lasst uns erfreuen" from the *English Hymnal* by permission of Oxford University Press. Simplified by permission of Oxford University Press.

God of Grace and God of Glory (#113)—Text by permission of Elinor Fosdick Downs. Tune ("Cwm Rhondda") © by Mrs. Dilys Webb, c/o Mechanical-Copyright Protection Society Limited, and reproduced by permission of the legal representatives of the composer who reserves all rights therein.

God, Who Stretched the Spangled Heavens (#100)—Text by permission of Catherine C. (Arnott) Cameron. Setting of "Holy Manna" reprinted from *Contemporary Worship 1: Hymns,* © 1969, by permission of the publishers for Inter-Lutheran Commission on Worship.

Good Christian Men, Rejoice and Sing (#52)—Text by permission of the Proprietors of Hymns Ancient & Modern.

He Is Born, the Child Divine (#17)—Text from "He Is Born, the Child Divine" by B. Wayne Bisbee, © Concordia Publishing House. Reprinted by permission. Setting for "Il est ne, le divin enfant" by Walter Ehret and George K. Evans, *The International Book of Christmas Carols,* © 1963. By permission of Prentice-Hall, Inc., Englewood Cliffs, New Jersey.

Holy Spirit, Ever Dwelling (#63)—Text by permission of Community of the Resurrection.

Hosanna, Hallelujah (#42)—Text and tune ("Hosanna, hallelujah!"), © 1967 by Richard K. Avery and Donald S. Marsh. From *Hymns Hot and Carols Cool.* Used by permission, Proclamation Productions, Inc., Port Jervis, NY 12771.

How Glad I Am Each Christmas Eve (#18)—Text by permission of Augsburg Publishing House.

I Was Made a Christian (#75)—Setting of "Adoro te devote" from *The Children's Hymnal,* © 1955 by Concordia Publishing House. Used by permission.

I Wonder as I Wander (#19)—Collected and arranged by John Jacob Niles. © 1934 by G. Schirmer (Inc.). International Copyright secured. Used by permission.

In Christ There Is No East or West (#112)—Text reprinted by permission of the American Tract Society, Oradell, New Jersey.

Let All Things Now Living (#77)—Text copyrighted by E. C. Schirmer Music Co. Reprinted with permission.

Let There Be Peace on Earth (#125)—Text and tune by permission of Jan-Lee Music.

My Song Is Love Unknown (#34)—Tune ("Love Unknown") is copyrighted and is reprinted here with permission by the successor to the late Dr. John Ireland.

Now Let the Heavens Be Joyful (#50)—Setting from *Carols for the Seasons,* © 1959 by Concordia Publishing House. Used by permission.

Now the Green Blade Riseth (#51)—Text, tune ("Noel Nouvelet"), and setting from *The Oxford Book of Carols* by permission of Oxford University Press.

O Little Town of Bethlehem (#26)—Tune ("Forest Green") and setting by permission of Oxford University Press.

Oh, Come, Oh, Come, Emmanuel (#3)—Setting of "Veni, Emmanuel" from *Our Songs of Praise,* © 1954 by Concordia Publishing House. Used by permission.

Oh, He's King of Kings (#59)—Setting of "Kings of Kings," # 1956, Neil A. Kjos Music Co., Park Ridge, Ill. Reprinted by permission from *Youth Sings.* Altered by permission.

Oh, How Beautiful the Sky (#22)—Translation of text by permission of Augsburg Publishing House, Minneapolis, Minnesota. Setting of "Dejlig er den himmel blaa" from *Carols for the Seasons,* © 1959 by Concordia Publishing House. Used by permission.

Oh, How Joyfully, Oh, How Merrily (#25)—Text used by permission of the Reverend Paul W. Czamanske.

Oh, Nobody Knows the Trouble I See (#180)—Setting of "Nobody Knows," © 1947 by Simon and Schuster, Inc., and Artists and Writers Guild, Inc. Reprinted by permission of Simon and Schuster.

Oh, Take My Hand, Dear Father (#142)—Translation of text from *The Lutheran Service Book and Hymnal* by permission of the Commission on the Liturgy and Hymnal.

Our Father, by Whose Name (#191)—Text by permission of the Church Pension Fund.

Our Father, Who Art in Heaven (#172)—Tune ("Hallowed Be Thy Name") from the Edric Connor Collection of West Indian Spirituals and Folk Songs. Copyright 1945 by Boosey & Hawkes Ltd.; renewed 1973. Reprinted by permission of Boosey & Hawkes, Inc. Adaptation of text and tune and guitar arrangement from *Songs for Today,* © 1964, the Youth Department, American Lutheran Church. Used by permission.

Prepare the Way, O Zion (#6)—Translation of text from *The Hymnal,* Augustana Book Concern, by permission of Fortress Press.

Sent Forth by God's Blessing (#126)—Text by permission of World Library Publications, Inc.

Shalom, My Friends (#127)—Translation of text from *Praise the Lord,* © 1973 by Concordia Publishing House. Used by permission.

Sing to the Lord of Harvest (#108)—Setting of "Wie lieblich ist der Maien" from "Sing to the Lord of Harvest," © 1973 by Concordia Publishing House. Used by permission.

Singing for Jesus (#78)—Setting of "Slane" by permission of Augsburg Publishing House.

Spring Has Now Unwrapped the Flowers (#58)—Text from *The Oxford Book of Carols* by permission of Oxford University Press.

Thanks Be to God (#99)—Text, tune ("Thanks Be to God"), and setting by permission of John Ylvisaker.

The King of Glory (#40)—Text © 1967 by Willard F. Jabusch, St. Mary of the Lake Seminary, Mundelein, Illinois 60060.

The True Light that Enlightens Man (#73)—Text by permission of John Ylvisaker.

This Is a Joyous, Happy Day (#76)—Text by Roger Lauren Tappert (b. 1941), alt. From *New Blades of Grass*. Copyright Roger Lauren Tappert 1971. Used by permission. Setting of "Lasst uns erfreuen" from the *English Hymnal* by permission of Oxford University Press. Simplified by permission of Oxford University Press.

This Joyful Eastertide (#46)—Text by permission of A. R. Mowbray & Co., Ltd.

This Night My Soul Has Caught New Fire (#184)—Guitar arrangement of "Satan's Kingdom Tumbling" by permission of Ted Wuerffel.

Thy Strong Word Did Cleave the Darkness (#87)—Tune ("Ebenezer") copyright owner untraceable.

Wake Us, O Lord, to Human Need (#109)—Text by permission of Phyllis Kersten.

We Thank You, Lord, for Eyes to See (#111)—Words from *As Children Worship* by Jeanette E. Perkins. Copyright 1936, 1964, The Pilgrim Press. Used by permission of United Church Press.

Were You There (#39)—Guitar arrangement of "Were You There" by permission of Ted Wuerffel.

Whatsoever You Do (#117)—Text and tune ("Whatsoever You Do"), copyright 1967 by Willard F. Jabusch, St. Mary of the Lake Seminary, Mundelein, Illinois 60060.

Acknowledgment is hereby expressed to Theodore Wuerffel for his assistance in preparing many of the guitar arrangements for this hymnal.

Scripture passages included in the body of hymns are taken from *Psalms/Now*, Leslie Brandt, © 1973, Concordia Publishing House, and from *Epistles/Now*, Leslie Brandt, © 1974, Concordia Publishing House. Used by permission.

Every effort has been made to determine the ownership of all texts, tunes and harmonizations used in this edition and to secure permission for their use. Any oversight that may have occurred will be duly corrected and properly acknowledged in future editions if brought to the publisher's attention.